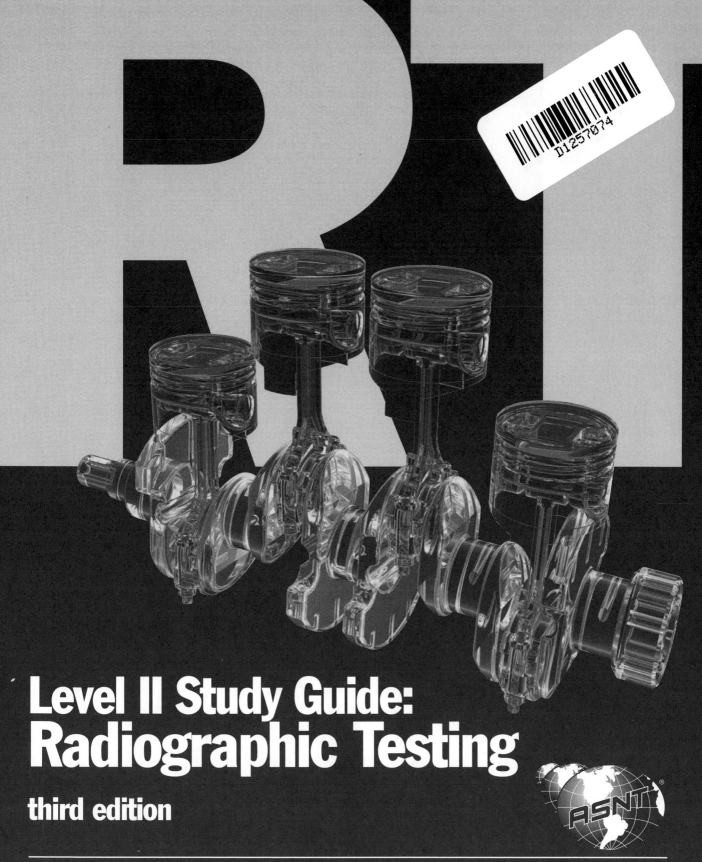

Level II Study Guide:
Radiographic Testing

third edition

The American Society for Nondestructive Testing, Inc.

first printing 04/12

Errata, if available for this printing, may be obtained from ASNT's web site, www.asnt.org.

ISBN-13: 978-1-57117-220-4

Printed in the United States of America

Published by: The American Society for Nondestructive Testing, Inc.
                 1711 Arlingate Lane
                 Columbus, OH 43228-0518
                 www.asnt.org

Edited by: Cynthia M. Leeman, Educational Materials Supervisor
Assisted by: Bob Conklin, Educational Materials Editor

Tim Jones, Senior Manager of Publications

ASNT Mission Statement:
ASNT exists to create a safer world by promoting the profession and technologies of nondestructive testing.

Acknowledgments

The third edition of the *Level II Study Guide: Radiographic Testing* builds on the work of the previous editions written by William Spaulding and George C. Wheeler. The content has been subdivided into four chapters for ease of reference. Material has been added regarding ionization of matter, scatter radiation, image sharpness, film handling and storage, and replenishment of darkroom chemicals, among other topics. As with prior editions, the goal of this study guide is to provide basic information to prepare a candidate for Level II examinations in radiographic testing.

Donald Blanchette of Mistras Group, Inc., deserves special recognition for his work in rewriting and revising this edition of the study guide. Thanks also goes to the following technical reviewers who assisted with this publication:

Brad Kienlen – Entergy
Michael V. McGloin – NDT Enterprises
Matthew Patience – Bureau Veritas
Robert Plumstead – Municipal Testing Lab, Inc.
Alejandro Vivas – Engineering & Inspections Unlimited, Inc.

Recommended References

The following references were used in formulating the questions contained in this book.

1. Bossi, R., F. Iddings, G. Wheeler, tech. eds., P.O. Moore, ed. *Nondestructive Testing Handbook*, third edition: Volume 4, *Radiographic Testing*. Columbus, OH: The American Society for Nondestructive Testing, Inc. (2002).

2. Staton, J. *Radiographic Testing Classroom Training Book*. Columbus, OH: The American Society for Nondestructive Testing, Inc. (2005).

3. Bush, J. *Gamma Radiation Safety Study Guide*, second edition. Columbus, OH: The American Society for Nondestructive Testing, Inc. (2001).

4. McCain, D. *ASNT Study Guide: Industrial Radiography Radiation Safety*. Columbus, OH: The American Society for Nondestructive Testing, Inc. (2009).

Other useful references include:

5. *Annual Book of ASTM Standards*, latest edition: Volume 03.03, *Nondestructive Testing*. Philadelphia, PA: American Society for Testing and Materials.

6. *ASM Handbook*, Volume 17: *Nondestructive Evaluation and Quality Control*. Metals Park, OH: ASM International (1989).

7. *Supplement to Recommended Practice No. SNT-TC-1A (Q&A Book): Radiographic Testing Method*, latest edition. Columbus, OH: The American Society for Nondestructive Testing, Inc.

8. *Radiography in Modern Industry*, fourth edition. Rochester, NY: Eastman Kodak Co., (1980). Available at: www.kodak.com/eknec/documents/87/0900688a802b3c87/Radiography-in-Modern-Industry.pdf.

Table of Contents

Chapter 1
Principles of Radiographic Testing

Radiographic testing unofficially began in 1895 when Wilhelm Conrad Röntgen, a German scientist, discovered that an unknown form of radiation emitted from a gas-filled electron tube was capable of penetrating objects that were opaque to light. After considerable investigation, Röntgen (Figure 1.1) named the rays *X-rays* to indicate their origin was unknown.

At about the same time, Antoine Henri Becquerel, a French scientist, found that radiation from certain uranium compounds had similar properties. This radiation was later determined by Ernest Rutherford to be two distinct types called *alpha* and *beta* radiation.

In 1900, Paul Ulrich Villard, also a French scientist, found that a third type of radiation emitted from some radioactive materials was similar to X-rays. This radiation was called *gamma rays*.

Figure 1.1: Wilhelm Conrad Röntgen.

X-Rays and Gamma Rays

X-rays and gamma rays are essentially the same, differing only in their origin. X-rays are produced artificially by accelerating or decelerating high-energy electrons using electronic equipment, while gamma rays are produced by the decay (disintegration of the nuclei) of radioactive isotopes.

Significant use of X-rays and gamma rays for industrial purposes began in the 1920s. Since then, industrial radiographic testing has become one of the most commonly used methods of nondestructive testing. Radiography is most often used for process control during manufacturing, to detect subsurface discontinuities in end products (e.g., castings, welds, ceramics, composite materials and electronic components) and for quality control inspections of electronic components (e.g., determining internal fits, alignments and/or gaps in

assemblies). Radiography is applied in building and bridge construction, aircraft aviation and aerospace, automotive and space components manufacturing, and aircraft overhaul, maintenance and repair. It is also used for inspecting piping and pipelines, refinery vessels, steel pressure vessels and storage tanks.

Advantages and Disadvantages of Radiographic Testing

Radiographic testing can be used to detect internal discontinuities in almost any material that is not too thick. X-ray machines capable of penetrating as much as 660 mm (26 in.) of steel, and greater thicknesses of other materials, are available. In addition to discontinuities, radiography can disclose internal structures, configurations, fluid levels and fabrication or assembly errors. In most applications, radiography provides an image of the test object that can be kept as a permanent record.

Isotopes are often used over X-ray machines because they are portable, don't need electricity and can access hard-to-reach places. Isotopes are also used in field testing because they have greater penetrating ability than the X-rays generated by most portable X-ray machines.

The major limitations of radiography are that the opposing sides of the test object must be accessible, precautions are required to prevent personnel exposure to radiation, and the configuration of the object must allow for the satisfactory formation of shadows of its internal structure.

Note: In ASNT Recommended Practice No. SNT-TC-1A: Personnel Qualification and Certification in Nondestructive Testing (2011), radiographic testing is considered a technique of the radiologic testing (RT) method.

Radiographic Principles

Radiographic testing is based on the detection of differences in the transmission/absorption of penetrating radiation by different parts of the object being radiographed. The differences in transmission may be caused by differences in the thickness or composition of the absorbing material. Sensors that respond to the ionization produced when radiation is absorbed are used to detect the radiation that passes through the object.

Traditionally, special photographic film was the most commonly used detection medium. As with a photographic negative, the regions of the film where more radiation strikes the film will be blacker after the film is developed. In radiography, this produces an image of the part that includes its internal structure and discontinuities. Electronic sensors that react to ionization (e.g., geiger tubes and scintillation devices) also detect X-rays and gamma rays, and are used more often in radiographic testing applications.

Most discontinuities effectively reduce the thickness of the object, locally, so that more radiation is transmitted at that point. When film is the detector, the transmittal of more radiation results in greater darkening of the film (i.e., the discontinuity image is darker than the remainder of the object as in Figure 1.2). However, some discontinuities, such as tungsten inclusions in welds, may absorb more radiation than the surrounding material, which will appear as lighter images on a radiograph.

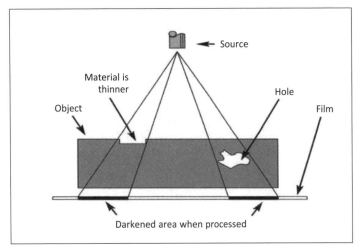

Figure 1.2: When film is the detector, the transmittal of more radiation results in greater darkening of the film.

Planar discontinuities that do not have any appreciable thickness, such as cracks and lack of fusion, are different. Because their small thickness causes little change in the amount of radiation that is absorbed, such discontinuities are difficult to detect unless the plane of the discontinuity is nearly parallel to the radiation beam.

Images of higher quality and greater sensitivity are generated through the use of higher quality films with a larger variety of film grain sizes. Film processing has evolved to an automated state, producing more consistent image quality by removing manual processing variables.

Electronics and computers also allow technicians to capture images digitally (Figure 1.3). Digital radiography (DR) captures an image that can be presented for interpretation immediately. Images can also be digitally enhanced and sent anywhere in the world. An archived digital image will not deteriorate with time. The advantages of DR over film include immediate image preview, immediate availability and a wider dynamic range that makes it more forgiving of over- and under-exposure.

Figure 1.3: Digital image.

Nuclear Atomic Model

The nuclear atomic model describes the atom as consisting of a small, relatively heavy nucleus (protons and neutrons) with electrons revolving in orbit around the nucleus (Figure 1.4). The volume of that portion of an atom outside the nucleus is very large compared to the volume of the nucleus itself or of the individual electrons; therefore, the greatest part of any atom is empty space. The difference in atoms of different elements is the number of protons in the nucleus. Electrically, the atom is normally in balance, the number of protons in the nucleus being equal to the number of electrons in orbit.

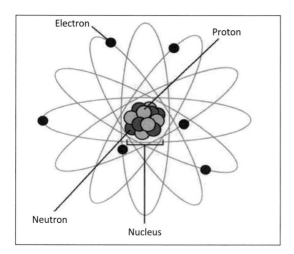

Figure 1.4: Atomic model.

Types of Penetrating Radiation

X-rays and gamma rays are a form of electromagnetic radiation like light, but their energy is much higher and their wavelengths are only about 1/10 000 that of light. The electromagnetic spectrum shown in Figure 1.5 compares the wavelengths and energies of various forms of radiant energy. The short wavelength and high energy of X-rays and gamma rays enable them to penetrate much more deeply into materials than light can.

The principal characteristics of X-rays and gamma rays are that:

1. the higher their energy, the shorter their wavelength, (wavelength is inversely proportional to energy);
2. they have no mass or electrical charge;
3. they travel at the speed of light;
4. when absorbed or deflected, they ionize matter;
5. the higher their energy, the greater the depth to which they can penetrate in a given material;
6. absorption is increased as the atomic number and density of the absorber increase;
7. they cannot be refracted (as by a lens) or reflected to any useful degree, but they can be diffracted by crystalline structures;
8. living tissue is damaged when it absorbs X-rays or gamma rays.

X-Rays

There are a number of advancements being made related to the generation and efficiency of X-rays, yet in general the principles are similar to conventional X-ray equipment. X-rays are produced when rapidly moving electrons are accelerated and then either stopped or changed in direction. Usually this is done in a vacuum (X-ray tube) by stopping the electrons with a barrier called a target (Figure 1.6).

This process produces characteristic X-rays, with energies/wavelengths that depend on the

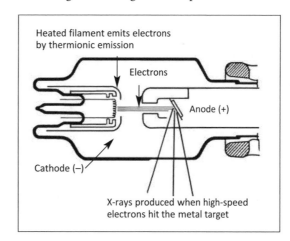

Figure 1.6: X-rays are generated in a vacuum tube.

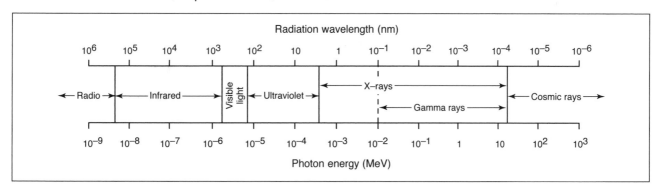

Figure 1.5: The electromagnetic spectrum.

target material, and bremsstrahlung X-rays with energies ranging from near 0 to the maximum energy of the electrons, the voltage at which the X-ray tube was operated (Figure 1.7). Bremsstrahlung X-rays are also called *white radiation* and make up most of the useful radiation in radiographic testing.

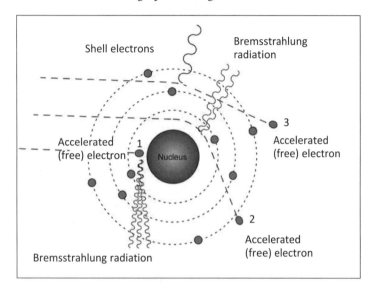

Figure 1.7: Generation of bremsstrahlung X-rays.

X-ray machines commonly used in radiography range in energy from 50 keV to 30 000 keV and in X-ray output from less than 0.05 Gy/min to as much as 250 Gy/min (5 rad/min to as much as 25 000 rad/min) measured at 1 m (3.3 ft) from the source. A typical X-ray tube consists of a source of electrons and a target in a vacuum chamber, with the means to apply high voltage across the source-target gap.

Electron Source

When electric current is passed through the wire filament coil in an X-ray tube cathode, the heat generated causes a cloud of electrons to be liberated from the coil. An increase in the current passing through the filament increases the number of free electrons, which increases the X-ray output of the tube. The focusing cup helps to keep the electrons bunched together to minimize the size of the focal spot, the area where the electrons strike the target. X-ray tubes contain two filaments that correspond to the focal spot sizes (Figure 1.8).

Figure 1.8: Filaments in an X-ray tube.

Electron Target

The target material must have a high melting point because it becomes very hot when bombarded by electrons from the filament. For the greatest efficiency in producing X-rays, the target should be made of a material with a high atomic number. Tungsten is generally used for the target material because it provides one of the best available combinations of high melting point and high atomic number, although other metals such as copper, iron and cobalt are used in tubes where special applications require a particular characteristic radiation.

Electron Acceleration

By applying a negative charge to the cathode and a positive charge to the anode, the negatively charged electrons are repelled by the cathode and attracted to the anode. The higher the voltage difference between the anode and cathode, the higher the velocity of the electrons when they strike the target, and the higher the energy of the X-rays that are generated. Higher energy radiation has greater penetrating power than lower energy radiation. In addition, as the energy of the electrons is increased, the quantity of X-rays generated increases.

In most X-ray machines, the X-ray output is measured indirectly by measuring the tube current (i.e., the flow of electrons from cathode to anode) usually in milliamperes or microamperes. In some machines, typically those with very high X-ray output, such as linear accelerators, the radiation intensity is measured directly in sievert (roentgen) per minute at 1 m (3.3 ft) from the target.

Because the production of X-rays is very inefficient, most of the tube current is converted into heat at the target. Consequently, the focal spot size and the cooling of the anode to prevent the target from melting, are major design limitations. In addition, the ability of insulating materials to withstand high voltages greatly influences tube design. As a result, some machines have a duty cycle rating based on the kilovoltage, tube current and length of exposure. In many industrial X-ray tubes, a rotating anode is used in order to help distribute the heat allowing the target to cool (Figure 1.9).

X-ray machines are usually rated by their maximum voltage capability in kilovolts or megaelectronvolts.

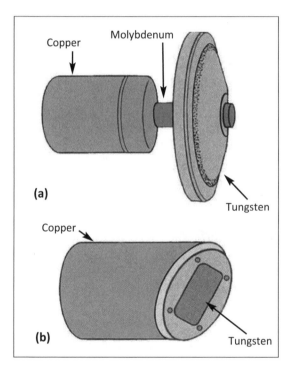

(a)

Copper
Molybdenum
Tungsten

(b)

Copper
Tungsten

Figure 1.9: Anodes: (a) rotating anode; (b) stationary anode.

Gamma Rays

Gamma rays are similar to X-rays but are produced by the decay of naturally occurring or artificially produced radioactive isotopes referred to as *radioisotopes*. Iridium-192 and cobalt-60 are the most commonly used isotopes for radiographic testing and both are artificially produced by neutron bombardment in a nuclear reactor. Until these radioisotopes became available after World War II, naturally occurring radium was used extensively.

The wavelength (energy) of gamma rays depends on the isotope. Each isotope produces one or more fixed wavelengths, but no bremsstrahlung radiation.

Radiation Energy

Gamma-ray sources are available in many energy ranges from about 10 keV to 12 MeV. The most commonly used are iridium-192 with energies of 310 keV, 470 keV and 600 keV; and cobalt-60 with energies of 1.17 MeV and 1.33 MeV.

Source Activity

The activity of a gamma-ray source depends on the amount of radioactive material present and its rate of decay. The rate of decay is measured in becquerels (curies) and is a useful way of comparing the strength of various sources of the same isotope.

Specific Activity

Specific activity is the activity per unit quantity of the source, expressed as becquerels (curies) per gram. It is useful in radiographic testing because a source of a given strength with a high specific activity is physically smaller than one with a lower specific activity. The smaller source permits a smaller source-to-film distance than a larger source, everything being equal. Also, at the same distance, the smaller source produces sharper images. (See Sharpness on p. 12.)

Radiation Intensity

The intensity of radiation from an isotope source (or from a X-ray source) is measured in sievert (roentgen) per unit of time at a standard distance from the source. For isotopes, the units are usually sievert/h at 1 m (roentgen/h at 1 m) as compared to X-rays that are usually measured in sievert/min at 1 m (roentgen/min at 1 m). The intensity from an X-ray tube is also often expressed in terms of the tube current with units such as milliamperes.

Half-Life

The number of active atoms in a source diminishes with time because of radioactive decay. The time it takes the radioactive material to decay to one-half of its initial activity is called the half-life of the isotope.

- Half-life of Ir-192: 75 days.
- Half-life of Co-60: 5.3 years.

This means that 1.9 TBq (50 Ci) of iridium-192 will decay to 1 TBq (25 Ci) in 75 days, to 0.5 TBq (12.5 Ci) in the next 75 days and so on.

Interactions of Radiation with Matter

X-rays and gamma rays have no mass or weight; they are bundles of energy called photons that travel at the speed of light. They can be absorbed or deflected by matter in a number of ways, usually by causing atoms of the matter to become ionized (electrically charged). Electrons and/or lower energy photons are emitted from the atom in a different direction from that of the incident photons. These electrons or photons may, in turn, cause the ionization of other atoms in the absorber.

Ionization

Any action that disrupts the electrical balance of an atom and produces ions is called ionization. Atoms with a positive or negative charge are called ions. Free electrons are negative ions and free particles carrying positive charges, such as protons, are positive ions.

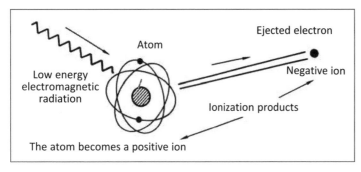

Figure 1.10: Ionization.

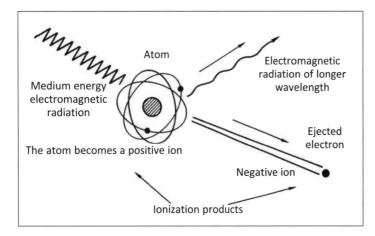

Figure 1.11: Compton effect.

X-rays passing through matter alter the electrical balance of atoms through ionization (Figure 1.10).

The energy of the ray may dislodge an electron from an atom and temporarily free an electron. The first atom (positively charged) and the electron (negatively charged) are, respectively, positive and negative ions, also known as an ion pair. In this manner, X-rays cause ionization in all material in their path.

In passing through matter, X-rays lose energy to atoms by ionization processes known as the *photoelectric effect*, the *compton effect* and *pair production*.

Photoelectric Effect

When X-rays (photons) of relatively low energy of 0.5 MeV or less pass through matter, the photon energy may be transferred to an orbital electron, ejecting it from its orbit. This phenomenon is known as the *photoelectric effect* or absorption. The remainder of the energy gives velocity to the electron. The photoelectric process absorbs all of the energy of the photon. It is this absorption effect that makes radiography possible.

Compton Effect

As shown in Figure 1.11, when higher energy photons of 0.1 MeV to 3 MeV pass through matter, scattering occurs due to the *compton effect*.

Part of the photon energy is expended in ejecting an orbital electron and imparting velocity to it. The remainder, as a lower energy photon, continues onward at an angle to the original photon path. This process, progressively weakening the photon, is repeated until the photoelectric effect completely absorbs the last photon.

Pair Production

Pair production occurs only with high-energy photons of 1.02 MeV or more, as shown in Figure 1.12. At these energy levels, when the photon approaches the nucleus of an atom, it changes from energy to an electron-positron pair. Positrons carry a positive charge, have the same mass as electrons and are extremely shortlived. They combine at the end of their path with an electron to emit one 0.51 MeV photon subject to the compton effect and the photoelectric effect.

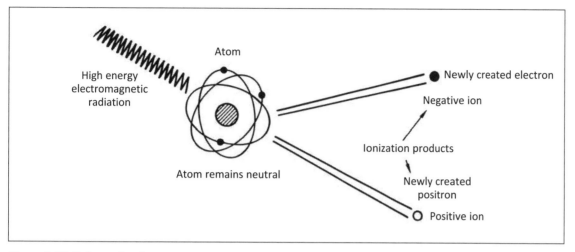

Figure 1.12: Pair production.

Scatter Radiation

The three processes — photoelectric effect, compton effect and pair production — all liberate electrons that move with different velocities in various directions. Because X-rays are generated whenever free electrons collide with matter, it follows that X-rays in passing through matter cause the generation of secondary X-rays. These secondary X-rays are a minor component of what is known as scatter radiation or scatter. The major component of scatter is the low-energy rays represented by photons weakened in the compton-effect process. Scatter radiation is of uniformly low-level energy content and of random direction.

Internal Scatter

The scatter that occurs in the object being radiographed, as shown in Figure 1.13, is called internal scatter. It is reasonably uniform throughout a test object of one thickness but affects definition by blurring the image outline. The scatter radiation shown in Figure 1.13 obscures the edges of the test object and the hole through it. The increase in radiation passing through matter caused by scatter in the forward direction is known as *buildup*.

Sidescatter

The scattering of rays from walls of objects in the vicinity of the test object or from portions of the test object that cause rays to enter the sides of the test object is sidescatter. As shown in Figure 1.14, sidescatter obscures the image outline just as internal scatter does.

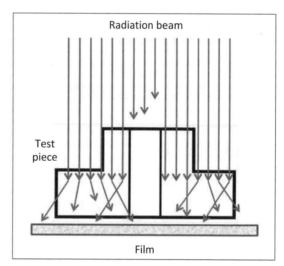

Figure 1.13: Internal scatter.

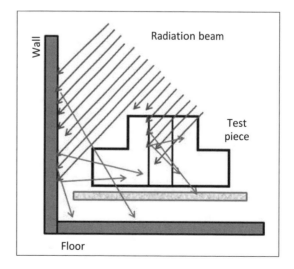

Figure 1.14: Sidescatter.

Backscatter

The scattering of rays from surfaces or objects beneath or behind the test object, as shown in Figure 1.15, is backscatter. Backscatter also obscures the test object image.

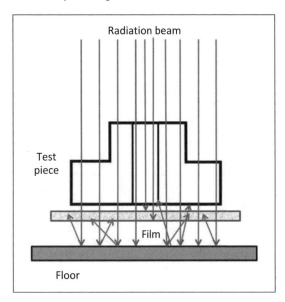

Figure 1.15: Backscatter.

Chapter 1: Review Questions

1. Which of the following is a false statement regarding the characteristics of X-ray and gamma rays?

   a. Living tissue is damaged when it absorbs X-rays or gamma rays.
   b. Absorption is decreased as the atomic number and density of the absorber increases.
   c. The higher their energy, the greater the depth to which they can penetrate in a given material.
   d. The higher their energy, the shorter their wavelengths.

2. What would be the result if the wavelength of the X-ray was to increase?

   a. Only fine-grain film would be able to be used.
   b. The heat on target would increase.
   c. The penetration of the beam would increase.
   d. The penetration of the beam would decrease.

3. Charged particles passing through matter lose energy primarily because of:

   a. scatter radiation
   b. ionization
   c. secondary scatter
   d. charged electrons

4. When electrons of many different energies strike a target, a continuous spectrum of X-rays is generated. These X-rays are known as:

   a. bremsstrahlung
   b. compton X-rays
   c. scattering
   d. slow electron emission

5. You have an Ir-192 source whose strength was 3.7 TBq (100 Ci) on July 1. What will be its approximate strength on Sept. 13 the same year if the half-life of Ir-192 is 75 days?

   a. 1 TBq (30 Ci)
   b. 1.9 TBq (50 Ci)
   c. 2.6 TBq (70 Ci)
   d. 3.3 TBq (90 Ci)

6. After three half-lives have elapsed, what will be the strength of an isotope source relative to its original strength?

   a. 25% of the original
   b. 33% of the original
   c. 12.5% of the original
   d. 11% of the original

7. What radioisotope has a gamma-ray energy emission that is approximately equal to 320 kV radiation from an X-ray tube?

   a. Co-60
   b. Ir-192
   c. Cs-137
   d. Ur-238

8. The specific activity of a gamma-ray source is important because it determines:

   a. the size of source required for a given activity
   b. the energy of the radiation that will be emitted
   c. the rate at which the specific isotope decays
   d. which type of radiation (alpha, beta or gamma) it will emit

Chapter 2
Radiographic Film Exposures

A radiograph is the shadow picture produced by X-ray or gamma radiation that has passed through an object and been partly absorbed by film. The radiation that is absorbed in the film sensitizes the silver halides in the emulsion in such a way that development converts them to silver particles.

In the film areas exposed to higher levels of radiation, more silver particles are produced by development, making the film darker. Film areas exposed to less radiation, due to a thicker or more absorptive object material, are lighter after processing, as shown in Figure 2.1.

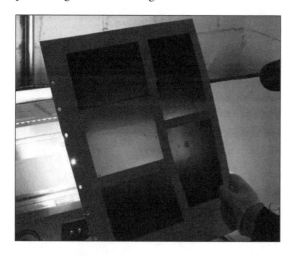

Figure 2.1: Radiographic image.

Film Density

The degree of film darkening is called *film density*. It is measured by the amount of visible light that can penetrate the film (Figure 2.2).

Density is defined as the logarithm of the amount of light incident on one side of the film divided by the amount of light transmitted through the film. Mathematically, density is presented as:

$$D = \log\left(I_o / I_t\right)$$

Equation 1

where:
D = density
I_o = light intensity incident on the film
I_t = light intensity transmitted

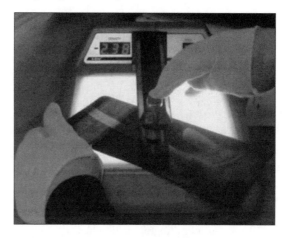

Figure 2.2: Measuring film density.

Film density and exposure time are related. Exposure is the intensity of radiation multiplied by the time it takes to produce a particular density. Thus, exposure is related to the time the film is exposed to penetrating radiation. All factors being equal, the longer the film is exposed to the penetrating radiation, the darker the density will be on the developed radiograph.

Image Quality

The usefulness of any radiograph depends on the quality of the image or the sensitivity. Sensitivity is defined as the smallest detail of the object that can be seen on the radiograph. It is a function of the contrast and the sharpness of the radiographic image.

Radiographic Contrast

Radiographic contrast refers to the amount of contrast observed on a radiograph and is affected by subject contrast and the contrast sensitivity of the film. Radiographic contrast can also be affected by the unsharpness of the detected image.

Contrast is affected by the radiation level. Most reference books recommend that a radiograph should be made with the lowest-energy radiation or, in the case of X-rays, the lowest kilovoltage that will transmit adequate radiation intensities to the film. This is because long wavelengths tend to improve contrast. However, radiation energies that are too low produce excessive amounts of scattered radiation that washes out fine details. On the other hand, energies that are too high, although they reduce scattered radiation, may produce images having contrast that is too low to resolve small discontinuities.

Subject Contrast

Subject contrast is governed by the intensity of transmitted radiation through various parts of the object and by the amount of scatter radiation reaching the film. The amount of radiation transmitted through various regions of a test object depends on the thickness of those regions and on the radiation energy being used. Large differences in thickness produce high subject contrast; small differences in thickness produce little subject contrast.

Film Contrast

Each type of radiographic film has a characteristic relationship between the amount of exposure and the density that is produced by that exposure. The relationship is usually expressed as a graph or characteristic curve in which the density is plotted against the logarithm of the relative exposure, as shown in Figure 2.3. *Relative exposure* is used because there are no other measurement units that apply to all possible exposure conditions.

The log of the relative exposure is used to compress an otherwise long scale. A log scale has the added value that the same distance will separate the logs of any two exposures having the same ratio, regardless of the actual exposure values. This feature is useful in exposure calculations.

The slope of a film's characteristic curve is a measure of its contrast, while the curve's position left or right within the graph is a measure of film speed. The contrast is greatest where the greatest density difference is produced by a given difference in exposure, that is, where the slope of the curve is greatest.

Given the same degree of development, a film with a curve that lies to the left of another film is the faster film, because the left-most curve indicates that less exposure is required to produce a given density. The shape of the characteristic curve of a given film is not sensitive to radiation energy, but it

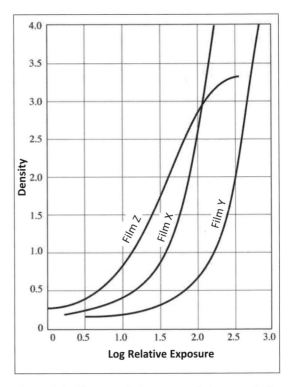

Figure 2.3: Characteristic curves of three typical X-ray films, exposed between lead foil screens.

is affected by the degree of film development, including time, temperature and composition of the developer. Within limits, an increase in degree of development increases the contrast exhibited by the radiograph.

Effect of Radiation Energy

Low-energy radiation produces high-contrast images because it is more easily absorbed than high-energy radiation. Therefore, only a small change in object thickness is necessary to achieve reasonable contrast. On the other hand, a large thickness difference is necessary to achieve reasonable contrast when using high-energy radiation.

Sharpness

The sharpness of a radiograph is usually judged from the image of known features such as edges, steps, or holes in the object. Sharpness is a function of geometric factors such as source size, source-to-film distance, object-to-film distance and screen-to-film contact, as well as the type of film and screens, and the radiation energy used. Unsharpness is also called geometric unsharpness, because that is the component of sharpness that can be calculated.

Geometric Exposure Principles

To create a radiograph there must be a source of radiation, a test object and film or some other type of imaging detector. A radiograph is a shadow picture of a test object placed between the film/detector and the X-radiation or gamma-radiation source. If the film/detector is placed too far from the test object, the discontinuity images will be enlarged. If the test object is too close to the source, any discontinuity images will be greatly enlarged, resulting in the loss of dimensional acuity. Proper placement of the film/detector minimizes enlargement and allows for more accurate representation of the size of the discontinuity.

The degree of enlargement varies according to the relative distances of the object from the film/detector. A certain degree of enlargement exists in every radiograph because some parts of the test object are always farther from the film/detector than others. The greatest enlargement is found when radiographic test objects are located at the greatest distance from the recording surface.

Enlargement cannot be eliminated entirely; however, with the use of an appropriate source-to-film/detector distance, enlargement can be minimized to a point where it will not be objectionable.

Figure 2.4 is a diagram of a radiographic exposure showing basic geometric relationships between the radiation source, the test object and the film/detector on which the image is recorded. These relationships are due to X-rays and gamma rays obeying the laws of electromagnetism. The ratio of the test object diameter D_0 to the image diameter D_f is equal to the ratio of the source-to-object distance d0 to the source-to-film/detector distance df. For the radiographic image to be close to the same size as the test object, the film/detector must be placed as close to the test object as possible and the radiation source must be placed as far from the film or detector as is practical.

Film/Detector Image Sharpness

The sharpness of the image is determined by the size of the radiation source and the ratio of the object-to-film/detector distance and source-to-object distance. Figure 2.5(a) shows a small geometric unsharpness (penumbra) when the test object is close to the film/detector. The umbra (darkest part of the shadow) is the only part that is normally seen in a radiograph. The penumbra (unsharpness) is seldom seen.

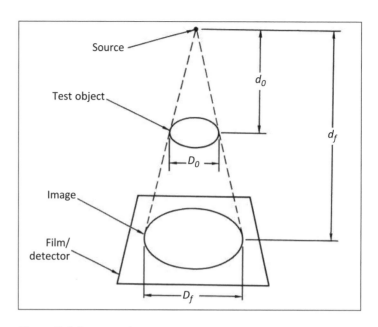

Figure 2.4: Image enlargement.

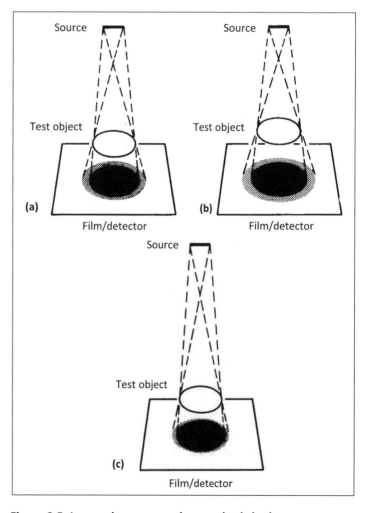

Figure 2.5: Image sharpness and penumbral shadow.

Figure 2.5(b) shows greater geometric unsharpness when the source-to-film/detector distance remains unchanged but the object-to-film/detector distance is increased. Figure 2.5(c) shows a smaller geometric unsharpness when the object-to-film/detector distance is the same as in Figure 2.5(a), but the source-to-film/detector distance is increased.

Most codes recommend maximum values for geometric unsharpness. To determine the geometric unsharpness, use the formula shown in Equation 2.

$$\frac{U_g}{F} = \frac{d}{D_o}$$

or

$$U_g = F\frac{d}{D_o}$$

Equation 2

where:

U_g = geometric unsharpness
F = the source size (the maximum projected dimension of the radiating source, or effective focal spot, in the plane perpendicular to the surface of the weld or object being radiographed)
D_o = the distance from the source of radiation to the weld or object being radiographed
d = the distance from the source side of the weld or object being radiographed to the film/detector.

Optimum geometric sharpness of the image is obtained when the radiation source is small, the distance from the source to the test object is relatively great and the distance from the test object to the film/detector plane is small. Figure 2.6 illustrates the decrease in geometric unsharpness with a decrease in source size.

Image Distortion

Two possible causes of film image distortion are shown in Figure 2.7. If the plane of the test object and the film/detector plane are not parallel, image distortion will result. Image distortion will also result if the radiation beam is not directed perpendicular to the film/detector plane.

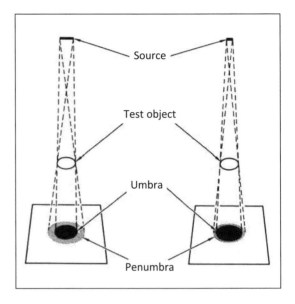

Figure 2.6: Effect of source size on image sharpness.

Nongeometric Factors Affecting Unsharpness

Unsharpness is also affected by the radiation energy, the type of film or other detector used, the type and position of screens and filters used, and the contact of the screens with the film. Increasing the radiation energy or increasing the speed of the film being used increases the unsharpness. Fluorescent screens increase unsharpness, while metallic screens vary in their effects depending on their composition, thickness and position relative to the film. All screens and filters that are within the film holder MUST be in intimate contact with the film or they will greatly increase unsharpness.

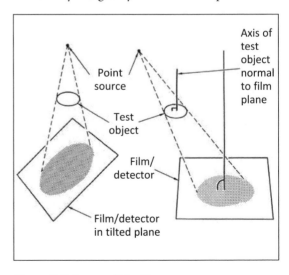

Figure 2.7: Image distortion.

Scatter Control

Because scatter radiation reduces contrast, it must be prevented from reaching the film or detector. The most common ways to reduce scatter are with *filters*, *collimators* and *masking*.

Filters

Filters reduce scatter in the entire radiation area by removing much of the less penetrating (softer) primary radiation while leaving greater amounts of the more penetrating (harder) radiation needed to produce the radiographic image. It is the most common technique used to reduce scatter. Because scatter radiation is less penetrating than the primary radiation, useful filtering can be accomplished with relatively thin sheets of an absorber such as lead. Many commercial film holders provide a 0.3 mm (0.01 in.) lead *back filter* to absorb scatter from material behind the holder, such as the floor or table on which the object and film are resting. For high-energy radiographic testing, thicker back filters are usually necessary. For many applications, front filters are often useful, but are usually specific to the application.

Collimators

Collimators reduce scatter by reducing the width of the primary beam, thus limiting the amount of radiation that would otherwise pass around the object and generate additional scatter.

Masking

Masking is performed by fitting absorptive material closely around the test object. The absorptive masking material is often made of lead sheets formed to the object, but copper, steel shot and even some liquids may be useful in specific cases.

Exposure Reduction and Intensifying Screens

The exposure time required to produce a desired radiographic image density can be shortened in many cases by placing intensifying screens in close contact with the film. Intensifying screens are constructed of materials that, when struck by the primary radiation, produce secondary radiation that blackens the film more effectively than the primary radiation. Fluorescent screens produce light, while metallic intensifying screens produce electrons and secondary X-ray photons. Fluorescent screens are seldom used with film

because they reduce the definition of the image. An exception is when very long exposure times are needed.

For radiographic testing with 150 kV radiation or higher, lead is the most common material for metallic screens, although other metals may be useful in some cases. Lead screens 0.03 mm to 0.3 mm (0.001 in. to 0.01 in.) thick are used up to 1 MeV to 2 MeV. For higher energies, lead screens as thick as 6 mm (0.25 in.) have been found to be useful.

Metallic screens may be used on one or both sides of the film and when two or more films are used in the same holder, thin screens are sometimes used between the films. In all cases, the screen surface must be kept very clean and free from foreign materials (e.g., grease and dust) because they can produce artifacts in the radiograph. Below 150 kV, a thin layer of lead oxide on a supporting material is often useful for intensification. Table 1 provides examples of maximum application thicknesses and intensifying screens.

Lead and lead oxide screens can shorten exposure times by as much as 2 to 2.5 times. Using lead and lead oxide screens with other metallic screens also provides useful filtration of scatter. Screens reduce exposure time and increase contrast, and should be used in most radiographic testing applications.

Principles of Shadow Formation

In order to produce useful images of the object, the radiographer must consider the principles of shadow formation in making the radiograph. Because a radiograph is a shadow image of an object placed between the radiation source and the recording medium, the shape, size and spatial relations of the parts on the image are influenced by the relative positions of the detector (or film), the object and the source.

Image Size

If the source of radiation is larger than the object, the image will be smaller than the object except when the object is in direct contact with the film. While most objects radiographed are not smaller than the source, the principal objective of much radiographic testing is to detect discontinuities. Since discontinuities may well be smaller than the source, and the thickness of cracks and lack of penetration is almost always smaller

Table 1: Standard X-ray machine thickness applications and screens.

Maximum Voltage	Maximum Application Thickness	Screens
<150 kV	Thin metal sections, electronics, ceramics, plastics	None or lead oxide
150 kV	127 mm (5 in.) aluminum, 25 mm (1 in.) steel Equivalent to 38 mm (1.5 in.) steel	None, lead foil or lead oxide
250 kV	Equivalent to 51 mm (2 in.) steel Equivalent to 76 mm (3 in.) steel	Lead foil, fluorometallic or fluorescent
400 kV	Equivalent to 76 mm (3 in.) steel Equivalent to 102 mm (4 in.) steel	Lead foil, fluorometallic or fluorescent
1 MeV	Equivalent to 127 mm (5 in.) steel Equivalent to 203 mm (8 in.) steel	Lead foil
2 MeV	Equivalent to 203 mm (8 in.) steel	Lead foil or sheets
8-25 MeV	Equivalent to 660 mm (26 in.) steel	Lead foil or sheets

than the source, this rule of shadow formation is very important to remember in searching for discontinuities.

If the source is smaller than the object, the image of the object will be larger than the actual object except when the object is imaged while in contact with the film.

Image quality indicators (IQIs) have a known size and are placed on the source side of the object, so the size of the IQI image is useful to estimate the source-to-object distance when the source size is known. Of course, when the IQI is placed directly on the film, this technique is negated.

The degree of enlargement may be calculated mathematically using Equation 3:

$$\frac{S_o}{S_i} = \frac{D_o}{D_i}$$

Equation 3

where:

S_o = object size
S_i = image size
D_o = source-to-object distance
D_i = source-to-film distance

Image Shape and Spatial Relationships

Image distortion occurs when the object plane and the film plane are not parallel. The preferred practice is to keep the film plane and the plane of the object that is of maximum interest as parallel as possible, even though this may distort the image of other portions of the object. *Note:* This does not mean that suspected cracks or lack of penetration should be oriented parallel to the film; they should be parallel to the radiation beam for reasons discussed previously in the Sharpness section.

Distortion of spatial relationships between parts of the object may also occur, as shown in Figure 2.8(a). For this reason, the preferred practice for most radiographic testing is to keep the center of the radiation beam perpendicular to the film or detector as shown in Figure 2.8(b).

Exposure

Radiographic exposure is defined as the intensity of the radiation multiplied by the time that the film (or detector) is exposed to the radiation. For a given radiation energy and source-to-film distance, the exposure may be calculated as:

$$E = MT$$

Equation 4

where:

E = exposure

M = radiation intensity (tube current or becquerels [curies])

T = time

Because the amount of radiation reaching the film through the object is unknown, the intensity used in the equation is the intensity of the X-ray or isotope source, as measured in becquerels (curies), rads/minute or tube current units.

For example, an exposure at 5 mA for 10 min would be equal to an exposure of 10 mA for 5 min. The units of exposure are determined by the units used for radiation intensity and time. In this example, exposure would have the units of milliampere-minutes. Values such as milliampere-seconds, becquerel-minutes (curie-minutes) and rads are also common.

While the output of X-ray machines can be selected by the operator within the limits of the machine, if using an isotope source, the radiographer must consider the half-life of the source in determining the output at any given time. For example, a satisfactory exposure of 3.7 TBq-min (100 Ci-min) required 1 min when made 75 days ago with a 3.7 TBq (100 Ci) iridium-192 source. A comparable exposure will now require 2 min at the same source-to-film distance because the source has decayed one half-life to 1.9 TBq (50 Ci).

Exposure Calculations

The density of a radiograph depends on the amount of radiation absorbed by the film emulsion and how the film is developed. The amount of radiation absorbed depends on the amount and energy of the radiation (primary radiation) that passes through the object, the amount of scatter reaching the film and the action of any intensifying screens used.

For any given radiation energy, the controllable variables that govern exposure are the source output, the time that the film is exposed and the source-to-film distance. Because the output of X-ray machines is proportional to the tube current, milliamperes or microamperes may be used. The output of gamma ray sources is measured in becquerels (curies).

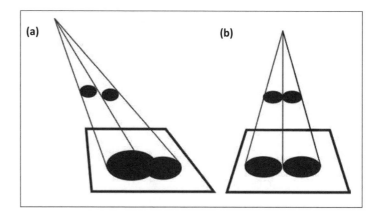

Figure 2.8: Geometric principles and spatial relations.

Exposure Factor

To make exposure values more general, the source-to-film distance may be factored into the exposure equation to provide what is called an exposure factor. As shown in Equation 5 (for X-rays) and Equation 6 (for gamma rays), the exposure factor is the exposure (E value) divided by the square of the source-to-film distance.

$$EF_x = \frac{M(t)}{D_i^2}$$

Equation 5

$$EF_R = \frac{S(t)}{D_i^2}$$

Equation 6

where:

EF_x = exposure factor (X-rays)

EF_R = exposure factor (gamma rays)

D_i = source-to-film distance

M = X-ray tube current

S = gamma ray source strength

t = time

The exposure factor (EF) is a quantity that combines milliamperage (mA) for X-rays or source strength for gamma rays, time (t) and distance (d). Activity is measured in becquerels (Bq) or curies (Ci). Numerically, the exposure factor equals:

$$\frac{mA \times t}{d^2} = \text{X-ray } EF$$

$$\frac{activity \times t}{d^2} = \text{gamma-ray } EF$$

For example, an exposure of 400 mA at 508 mm (20 in.) source-to-film distance has an exposure factor of 1 mA/in.², as does an exposure of 100 mA at 254 mm (10 in.) source-to-film distance.

Inverse Square Law

When no absorber is present, the radiation intensity from any radiation source decreases as the square of the distance from the source increases. In other words, the intensity is inversely proportional to the square of the distance from the source. This occurs because the radiation radiates as it travels away from the source, so that the same amount of radiation covers a larger area. Thus, the radiation is less intense farther from the source. Figure 2.9 illustrates this effect, which is known as the inverse square law.

Mathematically, this law is expressed as

$$\frac{I_1}{I_2} = \frac{(D_2)^2}{(D_1)^2}$$

or

$$I_2 = I_1 \frac{(D_1)^2}{(D_2)^2}$$

Equation 7

where:
I = intensity
D = distance

The inverse square law is very important in radiography because different source-to-film distances are often used for different radiographs. Source-to-film distance changes may be needed to satisfy image unsharpness requirements, allow for coverage of the object in one exposure or to modify the radiation intensity so as to adjust exposure time.

Radiographic Equivalence Factor

While many radiographic testing operations are performed on one type of material, other operations radiograph unusual materials. When unusual materials are encountered, it is useful to have a way to determine exposures for the new material based on exposure data for the well-known material. This can be done with a chart or table of radiographic equivalence factors similar to Table 2.

To use the table, choose the radiation energy of interest and the corresponding material of interest. Multiply the resulting equivalence factor by the thickness of the material to be radiographed. This results in a thickness value of either aluminum or steel, depending on the radiation energy, that has approximately the same absorption as the thickness of the new material. For example, at 220 kV, 13 mm (0.5 in.) of copper is equivalent in absorption to 13 mm (0.5 in.) × 1.4 = 18 mm (0.7 in.) of steel. To radiograph 13 mm (0.5 in.) of copper at 220 kV, use the same exposure that was used for 18 mm (0.7 in.) of steel.

Exposure Charts

Exposure charts simplify the selection of the proper values of the variables needed to produce acceptable radiographs. A common type of exposure chart is shown in Figure 2.10. As in all such charts, certain variables of radiographic testing have been fixed or predetermined. In Figure 2.10, the chart may be applied to film X with lead foil screens at 1.5 film density and 1 m (40 in.) source-to-film distance. Thus, the fixed variables are film type, source-to-film distance, screen type and thickness, and desired film density, while kilovoltage, material thickness and exposure are controllable variables.

The chart simplifies the relationships between material thickness, kilovoltage and exposure by

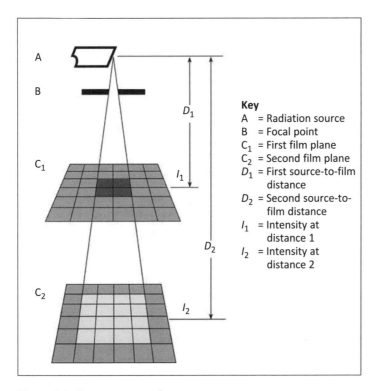

Figure 2.9: Inverse square law.

Key
A   = Radiation source
B   = Focal point
C_1 = First film plane
C_2 = Second film plane
D_1 = First source-to-film distance
D_2 = Second source-to-film distance
I_1 = Intensity at distance 1
I_2 = Intensity at distance 2

Table 2: Approximate radiographic equivalence factors[a].

Material	X-rays (kilovolts)								Gamma Rays			
	50	100	150	220	400	1000	2000	4 to 25 MeV	Ir-192	Cs-137	Co-60	Radium
Magnesium	0.6	0.6	0.05	0.08								
Aluminum	1.0	1.0	0.12	0.18					0.35	0.35	0.35	0.40
2024 (aluminum) alloy	2.2	1.6	0.16	0.22					0.35	0.35	0.35	
Titanium			0.45	0.35								
Steel		12.0	1.0	1.0	1.0	1.0	1.0	1.00	1.0	1.0	1.0	1.0
18-8 (steel) alloy		12.0	1.0	1.0	1.0	1.0	1.0	1.00	1.0	1.0	1.0	1.0
Copper		18.0	1.6	1.4	1.4			1.30	1.1	1.1	1.1	1.1
Zinc			1.4	1.3	1.3			1.20	1.1	1.0	1.0	1.0
Brass[b]			1.4	1.3	1.3	1.2	1.2	1.20	1.1	1.1	1.1	1.1
High-temperature nickel-chromium alloycoated		16.0	1.4	1.3	1.3	1.3	1.3	1.30	1.3	1.3	1.3	1.3
Zirconium			2.3	2.0		1.0						
Lead			14.0	12.0		5.0	2.5	3.00	4.0	3.2	2.3	2.0
Uranium				25.0				3.90	12.6	5.6	3.4	

a Aluminum is the standard metal at 50 kV and 100 kV and steel at the higher voltages and gamma rays. The thickness of another metal is multiplied by the corresponding factor to obtain the approximate equivalent thickness of the standard metal. The exposure applying to this thickness of the standard metal is used. EXAMPLE: To radiograph 12.7 mm (0.5 in.) of copper at 220 kV, multiply 12.7 mm (0.5 in.) by the factor 1.4, obtaining an equivalent thickness of 17.8 mm (0.7 in.) of steel.
b Tin or lead alloyed in brass will increase these factors.
Note: This chart applies only to one specific X-ray machine and the film processing time, temperature, and chemicals are also fixed.

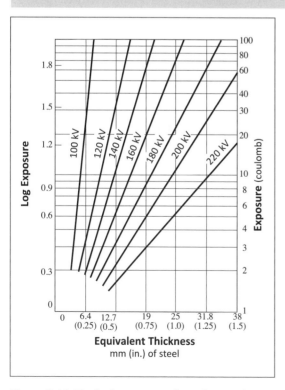

Figure 2.10: Typical exposure chart for steel.

fixing the other variables. This makes it easier for the radiographer to select exposure values.

For example, in the radiographic testing of a 25 mm (1 in.) thick steel part with this X-ray machine, 220 kV, 200 kV, 180 kV or 160 kV might be chosen. The chart shows that exposures would range from about 5.3 mA at 220 kV to 70 mA at 160 kV. If the X-ray machine were operated at 5 mA, the required exposure time at 160 kV would be 14 min, while at 220 kV, the time would be 1.06 min.

Charts in which other variables are fixed are also useful. For example, if the source-to-film distance, film, screens, density, film processing and exposure are fixed, a chart can be prepared that shows the relationship between kilovoltage and thickness for a given material.

Exposure charts for isotopes typically plot the exposure factor (rather than the exposure) against material thickness for various resulting film densities as shown in Figure 2.11. This type of chart reflects the need to allow for source-to-film distance variance to accommodate different

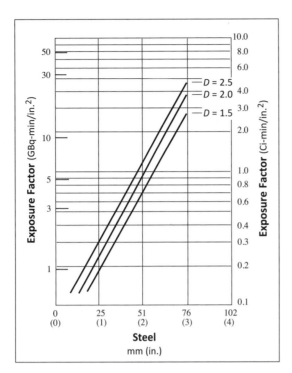

Figure 2.11: Typical gamma ray exposure chart for Ir-192, based on the use of film X.

thicknesses, because the radiographer cannot control the energy or the output of an isotope.

Deviations from some fixed variables of an exposure chart can be compensated for mathematically as follows:

1. **source-to-film distance** – use the inverse square law;
2. **film type** – use the characteristic curve of the films;
3. **desired film density** – use the characteristic curve of the film;
4. **film processing** – if characteristic curves for other temperatures, chemicals or development times are available, use them; otherwise, see item 2, below.

Changes to the following variables of the exposure chart cannot be accurately predicted:

1. **X-ray machine** – all X-ray machines are different; two X-ray machines operating at the same nominal kilovoltage and tube current may produce significantly different energies and intensities of radiation;
2. **film processing** – a change in chemicals, temperature or development time will change the resulting film density and contrast;

3. **type or thickness of screens or filters** – any change in the energy spectrum of the radiation reaching the film, such as those produced by screens and filters, may change the density and/or contrast of the resulting radiographs.

Object Thickness, Intensity, Distance and Time

The relationships between object thickness, source intensity, source-to-film distance and exposure time are mathematical and require that calculations be made or that the radiographer interpret charts. The calculations for changes in source-to-film distance, intensity, or time are simple arithmetic functions as demonstrated in Figure 2.12.

Variations in Object Thickness

An acceptable exposure of an object with varying thicknesses requires intelligent use of the radiographic testing variables. The use of filters or higher radiation energy will reduce contrast, but sensitivity may become unsatisfactory. Reductions in energy or removal of filters will increase contrast. The use of slower films increases contrast and sharpness, while faster films reduce contrast and sharpness.

For high subject-contrast situations, two or more films of the same or different speeds may be exposed simultaneously in the same film holder. The parts of the image showing suitable density on any one film are interpreted using a single film while two or more films are superimposed in order to view the lower density regions of the image.

Two films, usually of different speeds, that are loaded and exposed together in a single holder are sometimes viewed separately. The advantages of this technique are evident in situations where the material thickness or absorptivity cannot be precisely determined or where the object contains large differences in thickness.

Double or triple loading refers to the number of radiographic films placed in a single film holder. Different film speeds are used to obtain acceptable film densities over a wide range of cross-sectional thicknesses. Each film effectively images a separate area of interest that, when combined, provides total coverage of the object and enhances latitude.

It is especially important in the radiographic testing of multi-thickness parts to understand thoroughly how to use the characteristic curves of

Sample 1 is based on the following: initial exposure is 2 min, 5 mA, 20 in. source-to-film distance. It is desired to change the source-to-film distance to 36 in.

General Rule: The current, in milliamperes (M), is directly proportional to the square of the source-to-film distance (D).

$$\frac{M_1}{M_2} = \frac{(D_1)^2}{(D_2)^2} \qquad \frac{5}{x} = \frac{20^2}{36^2} \rightarrow \frac{5}{x} = \frac{400}{1296} \rightarrow 400x = 5 \times 1296 \rightarrow x = \frac{6480}{400} = 16.2 \text{ mA}$$

Sample 2 is based on the following: initial exposure is 2 min, 5 mA, 20 in. source-to-film distance. It is desired to change the source-to-film distance to 36 in.

General Rule: The exposure time (T) is directly proportional to the square of the source-to-film distance (D).

$$\frac{T_1}{T_2} = \frac{(D_1)^2}{(D_2)^2} \qquad \frac{2}{x} = \frac{20^2}{36^2} \rightarrow \frac{2}{x} = \frac{400}{1296} \rightarrow 400x = 2 \times 1296 \rightarrow x = \frac{2592}{400} = 6.48 \text{ min}$$

Sample 3

General Rule: The current, in milliamperes (M), required is inversely proportional to time (T). Using the results from Sample 1 and Sample 2, calculate for 10 mA.

$$\frac{M_1}{M_2} = \frac{T_2}{T_1} \qquad \frac{16.2}{10} = \frac{x}{6.48} \rightarrow 10x = 16.2 \times 6.48 \rightarrow x = \frac{105}{10} = 10.5 \text{ min}$$

The calculation may also be performed as follows:

$$M_1 \times T_1 = M_2 \times T_2 \rightarrow 16.2 \times 6.48 = 10x \rightarrow 104.98 = 10x \rightarrow \frac{104.98}{10} = \frac{10x}{10} \rightarrow 10.498 = x \cong 10.5 \text{ min}$$

Sample 4 is based on the following: initial exposure is 3.4 min, 75 Ci Ir-192 source, 18 in. source-to-film distance. Calculate the time required for 30 Ci.

General Rule: Time (T) is inversely proportional to source strength (S).

$$S_1 \times T_1 = S_2 \times T_2 \rightarrow 75 \times 3.5 = 30(T_2) \rightarrow 262.5 = 30(T_2) \rightarrow \frac{262.5}{30} = T_2 = 8.75 \text{ min}$$

Figure 2.12: Sample calculations.

films and the exposure charts for the available radiation sources. Proper use of these aids can greatly increase efficiency and reduce the costs and time for radiography.

Half-Value Layer

A half-value layer (HVL) (also half-value thickness) is the thickness of a specified material that reduces the intensity of radiation passing through the material by half.

The depth of penetration for a given photon energy is dependent upon the material density (atomic structure). The more subatomic particles in a material (higher Z number), the greater the likelihood that interactions will occur and the radiation will lose its energy. Therefore, the denser a material is, the smaller the depth of radiation penetration will be. Materials such as depleted

uranium, tungsten and lead have high Z numbers, and are therefore very effective in shielding radiation.

The half-value layer (HVL) is used to determine what thickness of a given material is necessary to reduce the exposure rate from a source to a certain level. At some point in the material, there is a level at which the radiation intensity becomes one half that at the surface of the material. This depth is known as the half-value layer for that material. Another way of looking at this is that the HVL is the amount of material necessary to reduce the exposure rate from a source to one-half its unshielded value.

Sometimes shielding is specified as some number of HVL. For example, if a gamma source is producing 369 R/h at 0.3 m (1 ft) and a 4 HVL shield is placed around it, the intensity would be reduced to 23.0 R/h as follows: $369 \div 2 = 184.5 \div 2 = 92.25 \div 2 = 46.125 \div 2 \approx 23$. Each material has its own specific HVL thickness. Not only is the HVL dependent on the type of material but also on the radiation energy. This means that for a given material, if the radiation energy changes, the point at which the intensity decreases to half its original value will also change.

Chapter 2: Review Questions

1. To produce an exposure equivalent to 5 mA at 305 mm (12 in.), what current is required if the source-to-film distance is changed to 609 mm (24 in.) and the exposure time is kept the same?

   a. 4 mA
   b. 10 mA
   c. 20 mA
   d. 40 mA

2. A source-to-film distance of 762 mm (30 in.) is changed to 609 mm (24 in.). What exposure time would be required if the original exposure time was 10 min?

   a. 2.5 min
   b. 5.0 min
   c. 6.4 min
   d. 15.2 min

3. Geometric unsharpness can be reduced by using a:

   a. larger focal spot size
   b. smaller focal spot size
   c. shorter source-to-film distance
   d. longer object-to-film distance

4. It is required that the radiographs of a part 102 mm (4 in.) thick must have a geometric unsharpness no larger than 0.4 mm (0.015 in.). If the maximum projected dimension of your radiation source is 2.5 mm (0.1 in.), what minimum source-to-film distance must you use to satisfy the unsharpness requirement?

   a. 66 cm (26 in.)
   b. 76 cm (30 in.)
   c. 91 cm (36 in.)
   d. 102 cm (40 in.)

5. All other factors being the same, radiographic sharpness or definition is improved by using:

   a. slower film
   b. faster film
   c. film with a larger grain size
   d. slower film with fluorescent screens

6. Other factors being the same, radiographic contrast is improved by:

   a. raising the kilovoltage and lowering the current
   b. lowering the kilovoltage
   c. using faster film
   d. adjusting the exposure to produce the minimum film density allowed

7. The minimum source-to-film distance needed to produce acceptable radiographs depends on the focal spot (source) size, the maximum allowable unsharpness, and the:

   a. type of film
   b. density of the object
   c. object-to-detector distance
   d. atomic number of the object material

8. Radiographic contrast is affected by which of the following:

   a. subject contrast
   b. sensitivity of the film
   c. unsharpness of the image
   d. all of above will affect radiographic contrast

9. Overall image quality of a radiograph is determined by its radiographic contrast and:

   a. definition
   b. density
   c. sensitivity
   d. latitude

10. What is the half-value layer thickness of aluminum for a radiation beam that requires 10 min exposure for 25 mm (1 in.) of aluminum and 20 min exposure for 38 mm (1.5 in.) of aluminum, all other factors being the same?

    a. 13 mm (0.5 in.)
    b. 25 mm (1 in.)
    c. 38 mm (1.5 in.)
    d. Not enough data are given.

11. The density differential between two areas of a radiograph is radiographic:

    a. sensitivity
    b. definition
    c. contrast
    d. filtration

12. The ratio of radiation intensities transmitted by various sections of a part as a result of thickness changes, is:

    a. subject contrast
    b. radiographic contrast
    c. sensitivity
    d. film gradient

13. What source-to-film distance is required to produce a maximum geometric unsharpness of 0.5 mm (0.02 in.) for an object 142 mm (5.6 in.) thick using a 5 mm (0.2 in.) focal spot (source) size?

    a. 1422 mm (56 in.)
    b. 1574 mm (62 in.)
    c. 2261 mm (89 in.)
    d. 2743 mm (108 in.)

14. A front filter at the film or at the source, or multiple-films in the same holder, are techniques that are used to compensate for:

    a. excessive subject contrast
    b. low density in thin areas of the object
    c. poor definition
    d. low subject contrast

15. For any given radiation energy, the controllable variable(s) that govern exposure is (are):

    a. the composition of the cathode
    b. distance from the anode to the cathode
    c. source output, exposure time and source-to-film distance
    d. material used to construct the vacuum envelope

16. At 100 kV, the radiographic equivalence factor for aluminum is 1.0 and for magnesium is 0.6. Approximately what thickness of aluminum is 51 mm (2 in.) of magnesium equivalent to:

    a. 17 mm (0.7 in.)
    b. 23 mm (0.9 in.)
    c. 31 mm (1.2 in.)
    d. 85 mm (3.3 in.)

17. If the source-to-film distance for a technique is modified from 762 mm (30 in.) to 1143 mm (45 in.), the exposure increases by a factor of:

    a. 0.44
    b. 0.67
    c. 1.50
    d. 2.25

18. The initial exposure time for a part was 3 min, 3 mA, 475 mm (18 in.) source-to-film distance. The distance has been increased to a 558.8 mm (22 in.) source-to-film distance. The milliamperes has not changed. What is the new exposure time?

    a. 3.5 min
    b. 6.5 min
    c. 4.4 min
    d. 2 min

Chapter 3
Film and Processing

Film and Film Handling

Industrial radiographic film consists of a thin sheet of transparent plastic called the base that is coated, usually on both sides, with photosensitive material called the emulsion. The emulsion is a solid, gelatinous material approximately 0.03 mm (0.001 in.) thick containing microscopic particles of silver halide. When the silver halide absorbs electromagnetic radiation, including visible light, it is modified so that the chemicals present in the developer solution can change the silver halide to metallic silver. The developer does not change the silver halide that did not absorb radiation.

After developing, the remaining halide is removed by photographic fixer, leaving just the metallic silver. Areas of the emulsion that contain little silver are relatively transparent to light, while those where there is much silver are less transparent, or denser.

Film Graininess

Microscopic grains of silver form the radiographic image. However, for various reasons, these particles tend to clump together in relatively large masses that are sometimes visible to the naked eye as graininess. All films exhibit graininess to some degree (Figure 3.1). Slow-speed, fine-grain films exhibit lower levels of graininess and higher definition, as is evident in Figure 3.1(b).

Graininess is reduced when the radiation energy that produced the image is low; increasing the radiation energy increases the graininess. Graininess is also affected by the film development process.

Film Selection

Choosing the right film for a particular application is important. The composition, size and thickness of the object; energy and output of the radiation source; the criticality of the inspection; and the required level of sensitivity must be considered when selecting the type of film. The time- and cost-saving advantages of higher speed films must be weighed against their poorer contrast and sharpness as compared to slower films.

The possibility of using relatively slow film but decreasing the exposure time by using intensifying screens must be considered. However, fluorescent intensifying screens should only be used when the highest possible photographic speed is required and the lower sensitivity can be tolerated.

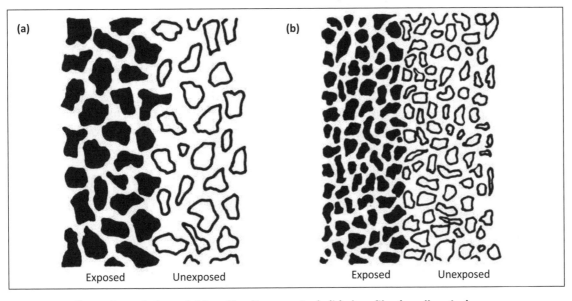

(a)   Exposed   Unexposed   (b)   Exposed   Unexposed

Figure 3.1: Film grain variations: (a) fast film (large grains); (b) slow film (small grains).

Available Forms of Film

Industrial radiographic film is available in individual sheets in a variety of sizes, prepackaged in light-tight envelopes or on large rolls. When smaller pieces are needed for confined spaces, individual sheets are easily cut in the darkroom; of course they must be inserted into a light-tight envelope and sealed before leaving the darkroom.

Prepackaged film is available in sealed, light-tight envelopes, with or without lead oxide screens. This film is ready for exposure without being removed from the envelope. Advantages of prepackaged film include the elimination of the time for loading film holders and its convenience in situations where a darkroom is not readily available such as in the field. However, compared to standard sheet film, prepackaged film is expensive.

Roll film is advantageous for inspecting large circumferential welds or other cylindrical objects. The film is wrapped around the outside of the cylinder while the radiation source is centered inside. Unless the object is extremely large, only one exposure is needed with this technique. The advantages of roll film for such work include reduction of the required setup time and reduction of the number of identification and location markers required.

Film Handling

Film must be handled carefully to avoid damaging the emulsion layers. Pressure marks, creases, fingerprints, scratches, static marks, humidity, heat, moist/contaminated hands and splashes or spills of processing chemicals can produce artifacts that may render a radiograph unacceptable. To avoid problems:

1. always wear cotton gloves when handling dry film,
2. handle it only by the edges,
3. slide it slowly (not rapidly) out of its box or film holder,
4. keep processing chemicals away from the loading bench, and
5. promptly wipe up any spills or splashes.

Store films in a cool, preferably air-conditioned location, away from penetrating radiation and store only the amount of film that can be used by the film expiration date.

Special precautions must be taken to prevent any exposure of white light to the radiographic film. It's a good practice to ensure that the box of radiographic film in the darkroom is completely secured or sealed with a dark tape to prevent any light from reaching the unexposed film. Light reaching the film will result in fog or dark images on the developed film.

Film Storage

X-ray films pose a challenge in the field of records management for two principal reasons. First, though rarely appraised as permanent records, they are frequently scheduled for very long retention periods, often as long as 75 years and, in some cases, even longer. Second, as film-based materials are vulnerable to damage from inappropriate storage environments, special precautions are needed to keep them in good condition until authorized for disposal.

Major factors affecting the archival properties of the film include temperature, humidity and the manner in which the films were processed.

Temperature – Continuous temperatures above 38 °C (100 °F) will accelerate staining caused by residual thiosulfate. Temperatures below the dew point of the air may produce condensed moisture on the radiographs and cause sticking. In general, a moderate temperature range is recommended. between 4.4 °C (40 °F) and 24 °C (75 °F).

Humidity – Extreme conditions must be avoided as prolonged exposures to relative humidity over 60% will tend to damage the emulsion with fungus growth and could cause sticking. Under conditions of low or changing humidity, emulsion adhesion defects such as edge peeling, flaking or cracking can develop. Low humidity will also increase the potential of static charges on the radiographs attracting solids that could harm them. In general, a relative humidity range of 30 to 60% is recommended.

Film-processing factors – If radiographs are not fully fixed and washed, they can retain some fixer, or thiosulfate, and some residual silver in the lower density areas. During storage, these residual chemicals can generate permanent, brownish stains superimposed on the radiographic image. Since the rate at which a stain is generated depends on both the amount of residual thiosulfate and radiograph storage conditions, factors such as the temperature, humidity and air flow in the storage facility must be considered as they affect this rate. If radiographs are stored at or below the upper limits of the temperature and relative humidity ranges, stain generation will be minimized and lowered as these two parameters are lowered.

Film Processing

After exposure, film must be developed and fixed so that the image will not deteriorate as it ages. Both developing and fixing are chemical processes that must take place in a darkroom or other location where there is little light or other radiation.

Developer chemicals are alkaline organic compounds that convert exposed silver halide into silver, while fixers are acidic inorganic compounds that convert the remaining silver halide into compounds that can be dissolved in water so that they can be removed from the film. Both developers and fixers also have other functions such as hardening the emulsion so that it is not easily damaged during processing and subsequent handling.

Darkrooms

Darkrooms must be lightproof, radiation-free and have a convenient, clean work area. White light and penetrating radiation must not be present in the darkroom because they can ruin any undeveloped film.

Darkrooms should be equipped with safelights (low wattage lights between 15 to 20 W, with red filters). Safelights should be 0.9 m to 1.2 m (3 ft to 4 ft) from any part of the darkroom where undeveloped film will be exposed. These lights provide sufficient visibility for cutting film, loading and unloading film holders, and manual film processing (Figure 3.2).

A workbench for cutting film and loading cassettes and film holders should be located a

Figure 3.2: Film-processing tanks with safelight. (Courtesy Scott L. Dean. Northwest Pipe Co., Washington, WV, Facility.)

considerable distance away from the processing machine or tanks. The bench must be kept clean and free from chemical spills and dirt that may scratch the film emulsion. In addition, it should be large enough to facilitate the workload. Sufficient storage areas for film, cassettes, screens and film hangars must also be available and conducive to the workflow.

In tank processing, as shown in Figure 3.3, the processing solutions and wash water are in tanks deep enough for the film to be submerged.

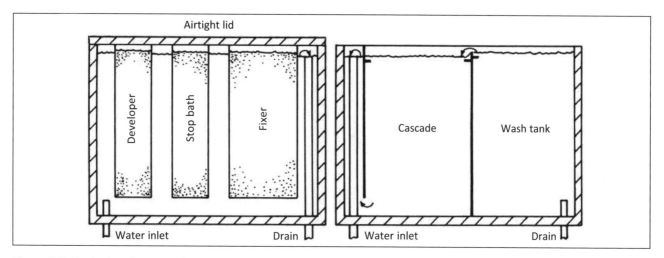

Figure 3.3: Typical tank-processing unit.

Manual Processing

For manual processing, the film is placed on a frame or film hanger. The film is then immersed in the *developer* for a time that depends on the temperature of the developer (Figure 3.4). Typically, development for 5 min at 20 °C (68 °F) is used for manual processing, with shorter times at higher temperatures and longer times at lower temperatures. The film hanger should be tapped against the tank immediately after the film is completely submerged in developer to dislodge air bubbles adhering to the film.

Figure 3.4: Developer bath with film on hanger. (Courtesy Scott L. Dean. Northwest Pipe Co., Washington, WV, Facility.)

During development, either the developer or the film must be agitated to allow fresh solution to contact the film emulsion frequently. Film developed without agitation will show uneven development and streaking.

At the end of the proper development time, the film is removed from the developer, allowed to drain for a few seconds and then immersed and agitated for 30 s to 60 s in a *stop bath* to halt the development process. Stop bath is an acid solution that neutralizes the residual developer in and on the film, and helps to prevent the film from streaking during fixing.

Next the film is placed in the *fixer* and agitated for 10 s to 15 s. When the film is initially submerged, the fixer takes on a cloudy, milky-white appearance that should clear in about 1 min if the fixer is at 20 °C (68 °F). After the fixer has cleared, the film should remain in the fixer for an additional

time equal to twice the time required for it to clear. Film that is not fixed thoroughly will discolor as it ages. Keep in mind that over-fixing reduces the image contrast and density.

After fixing is complete, the film is washed in running water with a sufficient flow to rapidly carry away the fixer. The emulsion should remain in contact with constantly changing water that covers the top of the hanger.

Effective washing of the film depends on a sufficient flow of water to rapidly carry off the fixer and to allow adequate time for fixer chemicals to diffuse out of the film. In general, the hourly flow of water in the washing tank should be from one to two times the volume of the tank. Under these conditions and at water temperatures between 16 and 21 °C (60 and 70 °F), films require about 30 min of washing. A general rule is at least twice the fixing time.

The film is then placed in a circulating warm-air drying cabinet, which should not exceed 49 °C (120 °F). Film should be removed from the dryer as soon as it is completely dry. A film is adequately dry when there is no moisture remaining underneath the hanger clips that could possibly drip down the film and cause streaking.

It is very important to control the temperature of the developer, stop bath, fixer and wash water during processing, and to time the exposure of the film to these liquids. The various processes occur at different speeds depending on the temperature. At temperatures exceeding 24 °C (75 °F), the radiograph may become fogged and the emulsion may be loosened from the base, causing permanent damage to the radiograph. Temperatures of 18 °C to 24 °C (65 °F to 75 °F) are preferable. If higher temperatures are unavoidable, precautions should be taken to avoid damaging the film. These may include use of special formulations of the chemicals or shorter processing times. Do NOT put ice in the chemical tanks because it will dilute the chemicals. It is also important to avoid having large temperature differences between the various liquids to avoid reticulation, frilling or other damage to the film emulsion.

Chemical Replenishing

Over time the film development process consumes some of the developer solution and causes the solution to become less active. Unless the solution is replaced, film sensitivity will gradually decrease. In order to obtain uniform radiographic results over a period of time, it is necessary to check the condition of the used developer solution and add developer replenisher in proportion to the quantity of film processed or at regular intervals.

The rate of replenishment varies with the size and quantity of film and the average density. The developing power of the developer decreases with increasing density or film size and vice versa.

If the reduction of developing action is the result of the processing of many films, it is possible to compensate for decreased chemical activity by using a replenishment technique. Most manufacturers of X-ray film developers provide for replenishment either by supplying a separate chemical or by providing instructions for mixing the developer to a different concentration from that of the original developer solution.

If a replenisher is added frequently and in small quantities, fluctuations in film density due to changes in chemical activity of the developer will tend to even out. However, if replenisher is added infrequently, a fluctuation in film density will become apparent, which may lead to considerable difficulty in consistently obtaining the required image quality in successively processed radiographs.

Automatic Processing

When a large number of films must be processed each day, a film processing machine or automatic film processor will provide economic advantages. Automated film processing reduces the manpower required in the darkroom, reduces the time required for processing and aids in ensuring consistent, high-quality processing.

Exposed film is placed directly into the processor without the need for film hangers. A series of rollers moves the film at a controlled speed through each step of the process. The processor maintains the chemicals at the proper temperatures, agitates and replenishes the solutions automatically, and dries the film.

Chapter 3: Review Questions

1. A significant difference between automatic and manual processing is that:

   a. the chemistry in automatic processors is more uniform
   b. manual processing is faster
   c. automatic processing is more reliable and cost effective
   d. developer time is not critical with automatic processing

2. The darkroom safelights for radiographic testing should have colored filters and frosted white bulbs, and be placed 1 m to 1.2 m (3 ft to 4 ft) from the darkroom work surfaces. What should be the wattage of the bulbs?

   a. 7.5 W to 15 W
   b. 15 W to 20 W
   c. 20 W to 30 W
   d. 30 W to 40 W

3. Because white light bulbs are used in darkroom safelights, the light must be filtered with a:

   a. blue/green filter
   b. red/amber filter
   c. dark filter of any color
   d. yellow/green filter

4. The loading bench in a darkroom should be:

   a. next to the film processing tanks or machine
   b. away from the film processing tanks or machine
   c. near the entrance for convenience in passing films in and out of the darkroom
   d. near the vent fan to ensure a good rate of air flow over the film as it is loaded in the cassettes or film holders

5. Static marks in radiographs may result from:

   a. using contaminated cotton gloves
   b. using noninterleaved film
   c. sliding film rapidly out of the film holder
   d. loading several films into one film holder

6. During the loading of unexposed radiographic film in the darkroom sealing the unused film back in the box with tape will prevent:

   a. light spots on the film
   b. exposure to light
   c. lighter densities on developed films
   d. burn out of lead identification numbers

7. The liquids used for manual processing should include:

   a. developer, stop bath,and water
   b. developer, fixer, stop bath and wetting agent
   c. fixer, stop bath and water
   d. developer, stop bath, fixer and water

8. Adding chemicals to restore the activity of a developer solution during normal use is known as:

   a. reactivation.
   b. replenishment
   c. restoration
   d. renovation

9. The basic purpose of a stop bath is to:

   a. cause development to cease
   b. speed up the fixing process
   c. enhance the alkalinity of the developer that is on the film
   d. prevent excessive fixation

10. The basic purpose of the fixer is to:

    a. soften the film emulsion
    b. remove the unexposed silver halides
    c. reduce the alkalinity of the developer
    d. neutralize the developer acids

11. Other factors being equal, processing film in solutions that are too warm may result in:

    a. lower densities
    b. mottling
    c. frilling or loosening of the emulsion
    d. uneven densities

12. The temperature of the water used during the washing process should be not be less than:

    a. 12.7 °C (55 °F)
    b. 10 °C (50 °F)
    c. 23.8 °C (75 °F)
    d. 15.5 °C (60 °F)

13. Using a wetting agent in manual film processing will assist in:

    a. the developing stage of the process
    b. hardening the film emulsion
    c. reducing water marks and streaks
    d. controlling film density

14. For best results, film should be dried:

    a. in ambient air
    b. by an oscillating fan
    c. in a dryer for a minimum of 2 h
    d. in a warm air dryer

15. The major advantages of automatic film processing are:

    a. fewer spills and splashes in the darkroom
    b. improved sensitivity of the radiographs
    c. reduced cost and time for processing
    d. speed, consistency and efficiency

16. Which of the following is a possible result of storing radiographs in a high humidified environment?

    a. The subject contrast will improve.
    b. There are no adverse affect upon the radiographs.
    c. Possible emulsion adhesion defects such as edge peeling can develop.
    d. The film density of the entire film will decrease.

17. Excessive density in a radiographic image may be a result of:

    a. excessive exposure time
    b. insufficient fixing
    c. the use of fine-grain film
    d. the use of an X-ray energy greater than 200 kV

18. In manual processing, low radiographic density may be due to:

    a. high developer temperature
    b. high developer concentration
    c. weak developer solution
    d. over-replenishing

19. Over-developing may result in:

    a. streaking
    b. fogging
    c. spotting
    d. lower density

20. Which of the following factors is most important in ensuring that satisfactory radiographs can be stored for years without becoming useless?

    a. Development beyond 5 min at 20 °C (68 °F).
    b. Using low pH stop bath.
    c. Thorough washing to remove all the thiosulfate.
    d. Fixing for at least three times the normal clearing time.

21. As the effective energy of the radiation increases:

    a. film graininess increases
    b. film graininess decreases
    c. radiographic definition increases
    d. film speed decreases

22. When a film is exposed to high levels of radiation, what impact will this have upon the silver particles on the film during the development process?

    a. No effect.
    b. Fewer silver particles will be produced by the development process making the film lighter.
    c. More silver particles will be produced by the development process making the film lighter.
    d. More silver particles will be produced by the development process making the film darker.

Chapter 4
Exposure Techniques and Radiographic Interpretation

Exposure Techniques

Whenever possible, radiographic testing is performed with a technique in which the radiation passes through only one thickness or wall of an object. This *single-wall radiography* requires that the source be located on one side of the object and the film on the other side, with no intervening material. Single-wall radiography simplifies exposure calculations and interpretation of the resulting radiographic image. Nevertheless, complex shapes and variations in wall thickness may make it difficult to select the proper radiation energy, filters, screens and film types, as well as film placement and other variables.

For large spherical or cylindrical objects where both the inside and outside surfaces are accessible, the *panoramic technique* is useful to reduce exposure time. Figures 4.1 and 4.2 show the general arrangement of the source and the film for a cylinder and a hemisphere. Although this technique is largely applied to welds, it is equally useful for parts of similar shapes that are not welded. The major requirement is that the wall thickness be relatively constant for all films exposed at the same

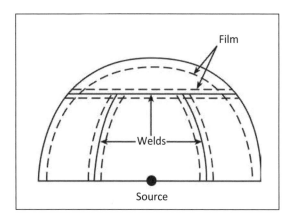

Figure 4.2: Hemispherical orange-peel head exposure arrangement.

time and that the source-to-film distance be sufficient so that the geometric unsharpness will be satisfactory using the intended source location. The panoramic technique is also useful for the radiographic testing of many small similar parts simultaneously, as shown in Figure 4.3.

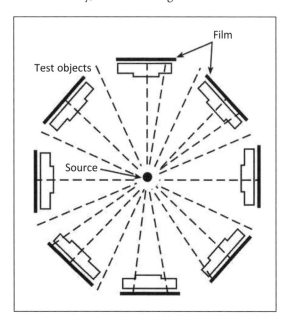

Figure 4.3: Panoramic exposure arrangement.

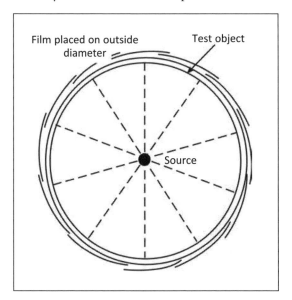

Figure 4.1: Weld radiography of larger diameter pipes and pressure vessels.

Radiographic testing of hollow parts (e.g., pipes and pressure vessels) often cannot be performed with the single-wall technique because either the source or the film cannot be placed inside the object.

When this occurs, it is necessary for the radiation to pass through two, and sometimes more, walls of the object. This is called *double-wall radiography*. Most specifications detail the requirements for double-wall radiography to ensure that adequate sensitivity is obtained for both walls and to assist in the interpretation of the radiographs.

Image Quality Indicators

Image quality indicators (IQIs) ensure that satisfactory radiographic image quality has been obtained. Often an IQI is a small test piece of standard design, made of material that is radiographically similar to the object to be tested. The IQI is placed on the source side of the object whenever possible and is radiographed with the test object.

Because it is placed on the source side of the object, its image represents the largest object-to-film distance and thus the largest unsharpness displayed by that radiograph. It is a good practice to provide the image of at least one IQI on each radiograph and, more often than not, it is required.

There are many standard IQI designs. The most commonly used are small plaques with holes (Figure 4.4) and sets of small-diameter wires. The dimensions of IQI features are some small percentage of the thickness of the object and image quality is judged by the smallest visible feature, such as hole size or wire diameter.

There are two plaque-type IQIs commonly used in the United States: ASTM/ASME IQIs conforming

to ASTM E 1025 and MIL-STD-453 IQIs. Wire IQIs conforming to ASTM E 747 are also used in the United States. These are similar (but not identical) to the DIN or ISO IQIs widely used in Europe. The image quality or sensitivity values obtained from the various types of IQIs are not identical, but they are mathematically related. The relationship for ASTM plaque and wire types is charted in ASTM E 747.

When specifications require particular types or sizes of IQIs that are not readily available, it is useful to be able to determine the characteristics of equivalent IQIs. ASTM E 1025 provides an equation and a conversion for determining equivalent IQI sensitivity.

Important: During typical usage, IQIs do not provide positive measurement of image quality. The IQI image on a radiograph indicates only that the image quality is not poorer than some minimum requirement. In addition, the IQI image is not intended to be used to judge the size or acceptability of discontinuities.

Identification Markers

Radiographs must be marked in such a way that each one can be identified with the object that it represents. For test objects requiring more than one radiograph, each one must be identified with the part of the object that it represents, so the film can be matched to the corresponding region of the object.

Lead letters and numbers placed on the object are usually used for this purpose because their high radiographic absorption allows them to be imaged on the radiograph. The exact locations of the lead markers may be permanently marked on the object or their locations may be keyed to a map of the object and retained as a permanent record.

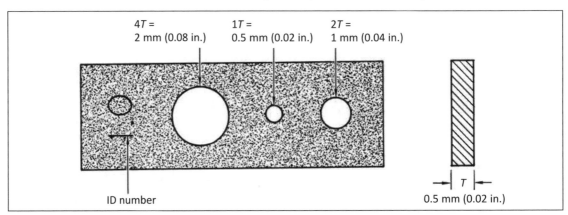

Figure 4.4: Standard image quality indicator for 25.4 mm (1.0 in.) material; *T* = IQI thickness.

Identification and location markers are essential in order to correlate the radiographic images of any discontinuities with their locations in the object. Specific requirements for marking vary considerably from customer to customer. Typical requirements are available in standards such as ASTM E 94, ASTM E 1030, various ASME codes and other specifications.

Discontinuity Depth Determinations

Knowing the depth that a discontinuity lies below the surface of a part can be very useful to personnel who must remove the discontinuity or to interpreters who must determine the part's acceptability. There are several radiographic testing techniques that can be used for determining the depth of a discontinuity. These include *stereo-radiography* and three *parallax techniques*: the *rigid formula*, the *single-marker technique* and the *double-marker technique*.

The rigid formula and single-marker technique both rely on making two exposures on the same film. They are useful only when the discontinuity has enough contrast to be visible on a double-exposed radiograph (i.e., one film exposed twice, with each exposure being half of the normal exposure time). The double-marker technique does not have this limitation, which makes it the most generally applicable of these three.

As shown in Figure 4.5, the double-marker technique uses lead markers placed on both the source and the film side of the object. Then, two normal exposures are made.

One film is exposed with the source in its normal position and the second is exposed with the source shifted an appreciable amount (20-30% of the source-to-object distance) parallel to the film plane. In the case of cracks, the source shift must also be parallel to the length of the crack.

The images of the source-side marker and the discontinuity will shift relative to the image of the film-side marker. The shift of the source-side marker will be proportional to the thickness of the object (the distance from the source side to the film side), while the shift of the discontinuity image is proportional to the distance from the discontinuity to the film side of the object. Knowing the thickness of the object, the distance of the discontinuity from the film side of the object can be determined with a simple algebraic calculation.

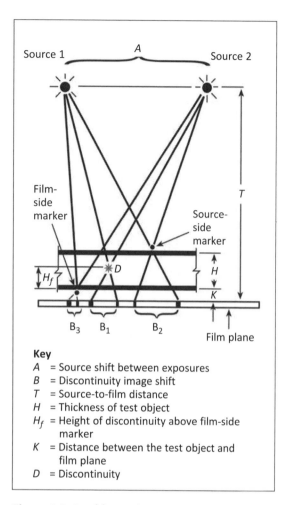

Key
A = Source shift between exposures
B = Discontinuity image shift
T = Source-to-film distance
H = Thickness of test object
H_f = Height of discontinuity above film-side marker
K = Distance between the test object and film plane
D = Discontinuity

Figure 4.5: Double-marker approximate method.

Interpretation and Evaluation of Radiographs

Interpretation of radiographs is the process of determining whether the radiograph is suitable for evaluating the condition of the test object. The interpreter must be familiar with the requirements of the governing specification with regard to film identification and location markers, image quality indicator size and placement, and film density.

Only personnel trained and experienced in radiographic testing should evaluate the condition of the object. The evaluator must be familiar with how the radiographic variables that were employed in making the radiograph may affect the image of the object and the image of the various kinds of discontinuities. The evaluator must be able to identify the images of various types of discontinuities and know which discontinuities are most likely to occur in a given portion of the object based on knowledge of how the object was made.

Visual Acuity and Dark Adaptation

The evaluator must have good visual acuity (the ability to see fine detail) and the ability to discern small changes in image density (i.e., low-contrast images). For this reason, most specifications require radiographers, interpreters and evaluators to have an annual examination for near-distance visual acuity and some require an examination for brightness/contrast discrimination.

No matter how good an individual's visual acuity and brightness discrimination may be, the ability to see low-contrast images is strongly affected by the light level to which the eyes have been exposed recently. For most interpretation and evaluation, it is sufficient to *dark adapt* one's eyes for at least 10 min by avoiding all white light. For the most critical work and for very low-contrast images, dark adaptation for at least 30 min is necessary. Repeated adaptation can be avoided by wearing red goggles when exposed to white light.

Even when sufficiently dark-adapted, a useful procedure to improve the visibility of faint images is to move the radiograph back and forth during viewing, because indistinct objects are more easily seen when moving. For example, it is easier to see an animal in the woods or fields when it is moving than when it is still. Viewing the film at an angle can also improve the visibility of faint images.

Viewing Conditions

In addition to dark adaptation, viewing conditions are very important to the interpretation of radiographs. The contrast sensitivity of the human eye is greatest when the surroundings are approximately the same brightness as the area of interest. Therefore, to avoid loss of dark adaptation and to provide the best conditions for seeing, the *film illuminator* must be masked to prevent bright light from escaping around the edges of the radiograph. For the same reason, when there are light areas in a dark radiograph, a *spot illuminator* should be used to prevent glare from the light areas. Lighting in the viewing area should be subdued and the viewer placed to minimize unwanted reflections from other light sources.

Film Density Measurement

The area of the radiograph under evaluation must be within a specific density range. Most specifications require densities between 1.5 and 4.0. However, some specifications allow densities above 4.0 provided that the illuminator is capable of supplying sufficient light to penetrate these densities.

Film density should be measured with a *densitometer*, an instrument that compares the intensity of the light transmitted through the film to the light intensity incident on the other side of the film. The densitometer should be allowed to warm up for several minutes and then be verified using a calibrated *density strip*. A series of density readings should be taken in the density range that is required for the radiographs that are to be evaluated.

Identifying Indications

Indications on a radiograph may be nonrelevant or relevant. Nonrelevant indications are those that were produced by:

1. features of the object that are intended to be present, such as its shape, including holes, ridges or steps in the object, or
2. errors in radiographic testing techniques, such as water spots, scratches or pressure marks on the film.

Indications caused by film handling or processing errors are often called film artifacts. A common method of aiding in identification of artifacts is to simultaneously expose two films of the same type in the film holder to produce two radiographs that are nominally identical. If the same indication is present on both radiographs, it is either an intended feature of the object or a discontinuity. Despite such aids, there is no substitute for experience in determining whether indications are relevant or not. Table 3 lists the common types of artifacts and their causes.

Relevant indications are those produced by unintentional conditions in the object, usually discontinuities such as voids, inclusions of foreign material or cracks.

Sources of Discontinuities

Discontinuities may be created at any stage during the life of a metal or other material — from its initial formation through the end of its service life. They are often roughly classified as inherent discontinuities, processing discontinuities or service discontinuities, depending on the stage during which they were created.

Table 3: Film artifacts.

Type of Artifact	Cause
Crimps (fold/bend)	Careless film handling technique
Static (tree branches)	Rough/rapid handling of film loading or unloading cassettes
Scratches	Handling, processor rollers (visible on film surface viewed with light at an angle)
Pressure mark	Heavy object placed on loaded cassette
Screen marks	Blemishes/contamination on screens (produce light image on film)
Light leak (light streaking)	Tears in cassette after exposure prior to developing
Fog (mottled film)	Exposure of unprocessed films to temperature, radiation, or light
Light leak (dark streaking)	Tears in cassette prior to radiographic exposure
Chemical spots/streaks	Manual process chemical splashing, no agitation in developer, no stop bath used
Processor pressure marks	Dark areas caused by contamination on rollers or improper clearance
Miscellaneous processing	Cross contamination of chemicals, air bells (cause false indications)

Inherent Discontinuities

Inherent discontinuities are those that were created during the smelting, refining, pouring and solidification of the metal into ingots, billets or slabs. They usually result from entrapment of foreign material, such as absorbed gases, oxides or sulfides, although some discontinuities, such as pipe are a result of mold design or pouring practices.

Processing Discontinuities

Processing discontinuities include those produced during processes that modify the shape and/or properties of the raw material, such as forging, rolling, heat treating, machining or grinding. Stresses and deformation are major causes of processing discontinuities such as cracks, bursts, laps and seams, although environmental factors such as temperature may also be a cause. Discontinuities in castings and welds also are usually considered to be processing discontinuities, although many of them are similar to inherent discontinuities because the processes involve the melting and solidification of metal.

Service Discontinuities

Service discontinuities are the result of stresses and environments imposed on the part during use. Cracking may result from processes such as fatigue, creep, thermal shock or stress corrosion. Pitting or general metal loss may be caused by corrosion, erosion, wear or fretting. Service discontinuities are usually open to the surface and, therefore, more economically detected by surface methods of nondestructive testing such as liquid penetrant testing, eddy current testing or magnetic particle testing. However, the affected surface may be internal to the part or in the inner surfaces of a sandwich construction and thus not accessible for surface tests. Radiographic testing may then be the best method of detection.

Identifying Discontinuities

It is very important to manufacturing and engineering personnel to know what kind of discontinuity caused a given nondestructive testing indication. Manufacturing personnel can use the information to try to prevent the recurrence of such discontinuities, while engineers are concerned because some discontinuities have more of an effect than others do on the usefulness and service life of an engineered structure.

Because the radiographic appearance of a discontinuity depends on shadow formation, the technique variables used in producing the radiograph have a significant effect on the appearance of the discontinuities. Therefore, accurate interpretation of radiographs depends on the training, experience and skill of the interpreter. Accurate evaluation skills can only be learned by extensive practice combined with a thorough knowledge of radiographic principles.

In addition to the influences of radiographic variables, there may be wide variations in the size and shape of any given type of discontinuity and discontinuities may be oriented in various ways relative to the radiation beam. As a result of these complexities, verbal descriptions of the radiographic appearance of various types of discontinuities are at best ambiguous and may be confusing. The proper way to become familiar with the radiographic appearance of discontinuities is to study the reference radiographs published by ASTM and other reputable technical organizations and gain extensive experience.

Examples of welding and casting discontinuities are shown in Figures 4.6 and 4.7, respectively.

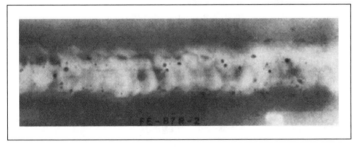

Figure 4.6: Coarse scattered porosity in a steel weld caused by entrapment of gas.

Radiographic Inspection Documents

In addition to the radiographs themselves, records should be made of the radiographic testing technique used, the results of the interpretation and the identity of the individuals involved. Specifications and contracts usually impose detailed lists regarding such records, but at a minimum they should include the following:

1. identification of the part or parts radiographed, including a drawing and serial numbers;
2. descriptive name(s) for the part(s);

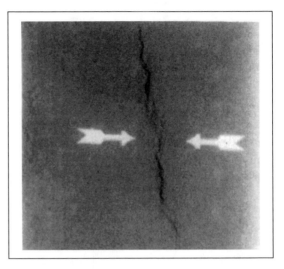

Figure 4.7: Hot tear due to uneven solidification of different section thicknesses in a casting.

3. governing contract or specification, if any;
4. type of material;
5. surface condition of the part when radiographed;
6. radiographic testing technique used for each exposure, including:
   a. identification markers,
   b. type and identification of radiation source,
   c. thickness of the material,
   d. source-to-film distance,
   e. image quality indicators used,
   f. film type, size and quantity,
   g. size and type of screens, filters, masking, etc., if any, and
   h. sketch or reference to identify:
      (1) location marker placement,
      (2) multi-exposure parts and area(s) radiographed, and
      (3) arrangement of source, part and film, including radiation beam direction;
7. evaluation results for each radiograph; and
8. signature(s) of the radiographer and the evaluator.

For repetitive work on identical or similar parts, it is useful to keep a permanent record of the technique used. This will not only reduce the time needed subsequently to determine correct layout and technique, but it will allow these details to be documented for each part by reference to the record, rather than repeatedly recording it for each part. This is often done by serially numbered shooting sketches or technique sheets kept in a permanent file.

Chapter 4: Review Questions

1. Unwanted marks and images that are produced during the processing of a radiograph are known as:

   a. anomalies
   b. irregularities
   c. artifacts
   d. relevant indications

2. A densitometer is an instrument that is used to measure the:

   a. X-ray density of an object
   b. depth of color of an object
   c. physical density of an object
   d. the density of the film

3. Densitometers should be calibrated before use by:

   a. taking a series of readings from a calibrated density strip
   b. using production radiographs with known densities
   c. measuring the reflected light from a radiograph
   d. using a photometer

4. Which of the following discontinuities would be classified as a "processing discontinuity"?

   a. fatigue crack
   b. heat treating cracks
   c. entrapment of foreign material
   d. thermal shock

5. When is it useful to use the rigid formula and single-marker technique used to determine the depth of a discontinuity?

   a. the length of the discontinuity is greater than 30% the thickness of the part
   b. the discontinuity has enough contrast to be visible on a double-exposed radiograph
   c. only for in-service type discontinuities
   d. for the detection of small rounded discontinuities

6. Discontinuities caused by fatigue and/or corrosion are categorized as:

   a. processing discontinuities
   b. inherent discontinuities
   c. service discontinuities
   d. metallurgical discontinuities

7. Which of the following is a type of image quality indicator?

   a. wire IQI conforming to ASTM E 747
   b. plaque-type conforming to ASTM E 1025
   c. plaque-type confirming to MIL-STD 453
   d. all of the above

8. Inherent discontinuities are those found in:

   a. forgings
   b. plate
   c. ferrous metals
   d. ingots

9. Devices used to ensure that radiographs meet the desired image quality level are called:

   a. image quality indicators
   b. location markers
   c. diaphragms
   d. shims

10. Crimp marks, such as folds and bends that appear on the developed film, most likely were caused by:

   a. poor handling of the film
   b. being exposed to light prior to development
   c. not using intensifying screens
   d. splashing fixer on the film before developing

11. For large spherical objects where both the inside and outside surfaces are accessible which technique is used to reduce the exposure time?

   a. Double wall technique.
   b. Contact technique.
   c. Panoramic technique.
   d. Elliptical double wall technique.

12. The cause of mottled film is likely caused by:

   a. unprocessed film being exposed to high temperatures
   b. tears in the cassette prior to radiographic exposure
   c. rough handling of the film
   d. pressure marks

Appendix A:
Radiation Safety

When the human body absorbs radiation, the ionization that is produced damages the body. If the amount of radiation absorbed is small and it is spread over considerable time, the damage may be temporary because the body is able to repair it, the same way it repairs bruises, scrapes or small cuts. However, if a large amount of radiation is absorbed in a short time, the damage may be permanent because it is too great to be repaired by the body. In extreme cases, death may result. Consequently, persons working with radiation must thoroughly understand the safety issues and what safety precautions must be taken.

In regard to safety precautions, two particular problems with radiation are that:

1. X-rays, gamma rays and other ionizing radiation cannot be detected by any of the human senses, and
2. the damage may not be apparent immediately; therefore, it is extremely important to follow all radiation safety rules.

Safety practices are based on known medical facts about how the body is affected by radiation.

The legal limit of radiation that an individual may be exposed to, and other requirements, are set by governmental bodies such as the United States Nuclear Regulatory Commission (USNRC) and various state bodies. Radiation detection instruments must be used whenever a radiographic exposure is made regardless of the radiation source. *Dosimeters, rate alarms* or *film badges* must be worn by anyone working within a radiation area.

Fixed radiation facilities must be surveyed before the first use, provided with permanent monitoring instruments and alarms, and periodically surveyed for radiation safety. Field radiation work areas must have clearly marked boundaries and be thoroughly monitored during operation. The size of fieldwork areas should be minimized as much as possible by use of devices such as portable shields and collimators to reduce the potential for accidental exposure of radiographers and other personnel.

Because some radiation regulations vary from state to state, radiographers must be familiar with the laws governing radiographic testing in the state where they are working.

Appendix B: Radiographic Conversion Factors

Traditional Units Converted to SI Units		
Traditional Unit	**Multiply By**	**SI Unit**
electronvolt (eV)	1.6×10^{-19}	joule (J)
speed of electromagnetic waves in a vacuum (c) = 186 282.4 mi/s	1609.344	$2.997\ 925 \times 10^8$ m/s
unified atomic mass unit (u)	1.66×10^{-27}	kilogram (kg)
curie (Ci)	3.7×10^{10} 37	becquerel (Bq) gigabecquerel (GBq)
rad (rad)	10^{-2} 10	gray (Gy) milligray (mGy)
rem (rem)	10^{-2} 10	sievert (Sv) millisievert (mSv)
roentgen (R)	2.58×10^{-4} 258	coulomb per kilogram (C/kg) microcoulomb per kilogram (µC/kg)
R/Ci/h at 1 m	0.27	mSv/GBq/h at 1 m
Ci·min/in.^{2}	50	GBq·min/cm^2
R/min (absorbed dose)	0.01	Gy/min
R/min (dose absorbed by body)	0.01	Sv/min
degree fahrenheit (°F) – temperature difference	0.556	kelvin (K) or degree celsius (°C)
degree fahrenheit (°F) – temperature scale	(°F – 32)/1.8	degree celsius (°C)
footcandle (ftc)	10.76	lux (lx)

Glossary

Absorbed dose: Amount of energy imparted to human tissue or a biological system by an ionizing event per unit mass of irradiated material at the place of interest. Absorbed dose is expressed in gray (Gy) or rad.

Absorption: Event where photons in a beam of radiation interact with atoms of a material the photons pass through and are reduced in energy by this interaction.

Accelerating potential: The difference in electric potential between the cathode and anode in an X-ray tube through which a charged particle is accelerated; usually expressed in kilovolts or megaelectronvolts.

Accelerator: (1) Device that accelerates charged particles to high energies. Examples are X-ray tubes, linear accelerators and betatrons. (2) Linear accelerator.

Acceptable quality level (AQL): Maximum percentage of defective units of the total units tested in an acceptable lot.

Acceptance criteria: Standard against which test results are to be compared for purposes of establishing the functional acceptability of a test object or system being tested.

Acceptance level: See **Level, acceptance.**

Acceptance standard: Reference object similar to the test object containing natural or artificial discontinuities that are well defined and similar in size or extent to the maximum acceptable in the product. See **Standard.**

Accommodation: Of the eye, adjustment of the lens' focusing power by changing the thickness and curvature of the lens by the action of tiny muscles attached to the lens.

Accommodation facilitates the viewing of objects near and far.

Activity: Degree of radioactivity of a particular isotope. Activity is expressed as the number of atoms disintegrating per unit of time. Measured in becquerel (curie).

Agency: Organization selected by an authority to perform nondestructive testing, as required by a specification or purchase order.

Algorithm: Prescribed set of well-defined rules or processes for the solution of a mathematical problem in a finite number of steps.

Alpha particle: Positively charged ion emitted by certain radioactive materials. It is made up of two neutrons and two protons; hence, it is identical with the nucleus of a helium atom.

Alternating current: Electrical current that reverses its direction of flow at regular intervals.

Alternating magnetic field: Varying magnetic field produced around a conductor by an alternating current flowing in the conductor.

Ampere (A): Unit of electric current.

Analog-to-digital converter: Circuit whose input is information in analog form and whose output is the same information in digital form.

Angstrom (Å): Unit of distance once used to express wavelengths of electromagnetic radiation. The SI unit nanometer (nm) is now preferred; 1 nm = 10 Å.

Anode: (1) In radiography, the positive electrode of a cathode ray tube that generates ionizing radiation. (2) Positively charged terminal, which may corrode electro-chemically during production of an electric current. Compare **Cathode**.

Artifact: False indication on a radiograph arising from, but not limited to, faulty manufacture, storage, handling, exposure or processing.

ASNT Recommended Practice No. SNT-TC-1A: See ***Recommended Practice No. SNT-TC-1A***.

Attenuation: The decrease in radiation intensity caused by distance and by passage through material.

Automated system: Acting mechanism that performs required tasks at a determined time and in a fixed sequence in response to certain conditions. Also called a robotic system.

Backscatter: In transmission radiography, interaction of radiation with matter behind the image plane such that scattered radiation returns to the image plane, often adding fog and noise that interfere with production of an image of the test object.

Backscatter imaging: In radiographic testing, a family of techniques that use backscatter for image generation.

Barium clay: Molding clay containing barium, used to eliminate or reduce the amount of scattered or secondary radiation reaching the film.

Beam: Defined stream of radiation in which all elements are traveling in nearly parallel paths.

Beam quality: Penetrating energy of a radiation beam.

Beam spread: Divergence from a beam of radiation in which all elements are traveling in parallel paths.

Becquerel (Bq): SI unit for measurement of radioactivity, equivalent to one disintegration per second. Replaces curie. One curie equals 37 GBq.

Beta particle: Electron or positron emitted from a nucleus during decay.

Beta ray: Radiation stream consisting of beta particles.

Betatron: Circular electron accelerator that is a source of either high-energy electrons or X-rays. The electrons are injected by periodic bursts into a region of an alternating magnetic field. Sometimes the electrons are used directly as the radiation.

Billet: Solid semifinished round or square product that has been hot worked for forging, rolling or extrusion.

Bremsstrahlung: Electromagnetic radiation produced when electrons' path and kinetic energy brings them close to the positive fields of atomic nuclei — as when electrons strike a target provided for this purpose. The electrons slow down, giving up kinetic energy as X-radiation.

Burst: In metal, external or internal rupture caused by improper forming.

Butt weld or butt joint: Weld joining two metal pieces in the same plane.

Camera, gamma-ray: Device that contains a sealed radiation source, where the source or shielding can be moved so that the source becomes unshielded (to make a radiographic exposure) or shielded (for safe storage).

Cassette, film: Lightproof container that is used for holding radiographic film in position during the radiographic exposure. The cassette may be rigid or flexible and may contain intensifying screens, filter screens, both or neither.

Casting: Object of shape obtained by solidification of a substance in a mold.

Casting shrinkage: Total shrinkage includes the sum of three types: (1) liquid shrinkage (the reduction in volume of liquid metal as it cools; (2) solidification shrinkage (the change in volume of metal from the beginning to ending of solidification); and (3) solid shrinkage (the reduction in volume of metal as it returns to room temperature).

Cathode: (1) Negatively charged terminal in an arrangement that produces current by chemical reactions. Compare Anode. (2) In radiography, the negative electrode of an X-ray tube, the electrode from which electrons are emitted.

Cathode ray: Stream of electrons emitted by a heated filament and projected in a more or less confined beam under the influence of a magnetic or electric field.

Certification: Process of providing written testimony that an individual (or test technique, process or equipment) is qualified. See also **Certified**.

Certified: Having written testimony of qualification. See also **Certification**.

Cesium-137 (Cs-137): Radioactive isotope of element cesium, having a half life of about 30 years and photon energy of about 660 keV.

Characteristic curve: The plot of density versus log of exposure or log of relative exposure.

Cobalt-60 (Co-60): Radioactive isotope of element cobalt, having half life of 5.3 years and photon energies of 1.17 MeV and 1.33 MeV.

Code: A written standard enacted or enforced as a law.

Collimator: A device of radiation-absorbent material intended for defining the direction and angular divergence of the radiation beam.

Compton scatter: Reduction of the energy of an incident photon by its interaction with an electron. Part of the photon energy is transferred to the electron, giving it kinetic energy, and the remaining photon is redirected with reduced energy.

Contrast: (1) In film radiography, the measure of differences in the film blackening or density resulting from various radiation intensities transmitted by the object and recorded as density differences in the image. Thus, difference in film blackening from one area to another. (2) The difference in visibility between an indication and the surrounding area.

Contrast, subject: Ratio of radiation intensities transmitted by selected portions of the object being radiographed.

Control: See **Process control** and **Quality control**.

Corrosion: Deterioration of a metal by chemical or electrochemical reaction with its environment. Removal of material by chemical attack, such as the rusting of automobile components.

Crack: (1) Break, fissure or rupture, usually V-shaped (the cross-section view that otherwise appears jagged) and relatively narrow and deep. A discontinuity that has a relatively large cross-section in one direction and a small or negligible cross-section when viewed in a direction perpendicular to the first. (2) Propagating discontinuities caused by stresses such as heat treating or grinding. Difficult to detect unaided because of fineness of line and pattern (may have a radial or latticed appearance).

Curie (Ci): Unit of measurement of the quantity of radioactivity. Replaced by becquerel in SI, where 1 Ci = 3.7×10^{10} Bq, or 1 Ci = 37 GBq.

Decay curve: Graph showing radioactive strength in becquerel (curie) as a function of time for an isotope. Decay curves are used in determining exposure times in radiographic testing.

Defect: Discontinuity that exceeds the acceptance criteria or is detrimental to the service of the test object. See also **Discontinuity**.

Definition: Description of linear demarcation sensitivity, or the detail sharpness of object outline in a radiographic image. It is a function of screen type, exposure geometry, radiation energy and characteristics of film or sensor.

Delamination: Laminar discontinuity, generally an area of unbonded materials.

Densitometer: A device for measuring the optical density of radiographic film.

Density, film: The quantitative measure of film blackening when light is transmitted or reflected, expressed as the log of the ratio of incident to transmitted light.

Depth of field: Range of distance over which an imaging system gives satisfactory definition when its lens is in the best focus for a specific distance.

Depth of focus: Distance a sensor may be moved from a lens system and still produce a sharp image.

Depth of fusion: Depth to which base metal has melted during welding.

Detail: In radiography, the degree of sharpness of outline of an image, or the clear definition of an object or discontinuity in the object. See also **Definition**.

Developer: In radiography, a chemical solution that reduces exposed silver halide crystals to black metallic silver.

Diffraction: A special case of scatter, where coherently scattered photons undergo interference or reinforcement, resulting in patterns indicative of the scattering medium. See also **X-ray diffraction**.

Discontinuity: Unintentional interruption in the physical structure or configuration of a test object. After nondestructive testing, discontinuities interpreted as detrimental in the host object may be called defects.

Discontinuity, inherent: Material anomaly originating from solidification of molten metal. Pipe and nonmetallic inclusions are the most common and can lead to other types of discontinuities in fabrication.

Dose: See **Absorbed dose**.

Dose rate: Radiation dose delivered during a specified unit of time and measured, for instance, in sievert per minute (or in rem per hour). See also **Absorbed dose**.

Dosimeter: Device that measures radiation dose, such as an ionization chamber.

Effective focal spot: Size and geometry of focal spot after target interaction. Viewed from along the primary beam central axis at the target, the effective focal spot would appear nearly square and smaller than the actual focal spot area covered by the electron stream.

Evaluation: Process of determining the magnitude and significance of a discontinuity after the indication has been interpreted as relevant. Evaluation determines if the test object should be rejected, repaired or accepted. See **Indication** and **Interpretation**.

Exposure factor: In radiography, the quantity that combines source strength (milliampere), time (usually minute) and distance. It is the product of milliamperage and time divided by distance squared and determines the degree of film density.

Exposure, radiographic: The subjection of a recording medium to radiation for the purpose of producing a latent image.

Field: In video technology, one of two video picture components that together make a frame. Each picture is divided into two parts called fields because a frame at the rate of 30 frames/s in a standard video output would otherwise produce a flicker discernible to the eye. Each field contains one-half of the total picture elements. Two fields are required to produce one complete picture or frame so the field frequency is 60 fields/s and the frame frequency is 30 frames/s.

Field of view: Range or area that can be seen through an imaging system, lens or aperture.

Film badge: Package of photographic film worn as a badge by radiographic personnel (and by workers in the nuclear industry) to measure exposure to ionizing radiation. Absorbed dose can be calculated by degree of film darkening caused by irradiation.

Film holder: See **Cassette, film**.

Film speed: Relative exposure required to attain a specified film density.

Filter: (1) Network that passes electromagnetic wave energy over a described range of frequencies and attenuates energy at all other frequencies. (2) Processing device or function that excludes a selected kind of signal or part of a signal. (3) In radiography, the thickness of absorbing material placed in a primary radiation beam to selectively remove longer wavelength radiation, thereby adjusting the quality of the radiographic image.

Fixing: Procedure used in film processing that removes undeveloped silver salts in the emulsion from the surface of the film, leaving only the developed black silver of the image on the film.

Focal spot: Area on target that receives bombardment of electrons. See also **Effective focal spot**.

Focus: Position of a viewed object and a lens system relative to one another to offer a distinct image of the object as seen through the lens system. See **Accommodation** and **Depth of field**.

Fog: Increase of film density caused by sources other than from the intended primary beam exposure. Heat, humidity, pressure and scatter radiation can all cause fogging of the film.

Fracture: Break, rupture or crack large enough to cause a full or partial partition of a casting.

Frame: Complete raster scan projected on a video screen. There are thirty frames per second in a standard video output. A frame may comprise two fields, each displaying part of the total frame. See also **Field**.

Gamma rays: High-energy, short-wavelength electromagnetic radiation emitted by the nucleus of a radioactive isotope. Energies of gamma rays are usually between 0.01 MeV and 10 MeV. X-rays also occur in this energy range but are of nonnuclear origin.

Geometric unsharpness: See **Unsharpness, geometric**.

Graininess: The visual impression of irregularity of silver deposits in a processed film.

Gray (Gy): SI unit for measurement of the dose of radiation absorbed per unit mass at a specified location. Replaces the rad where rad denotes radiation absorbed dose, not radian. $1 \text{ Gy} = 1 \text{ J·kg}^{-1} = 100 \text{ rad}$.

Gray level: Integer number representing the luminance or darkness of a pixel or, as a composite value, of an image composed of pixels.

Half-life: The time required for one-half of a given number of radioactive atoms to undergo decay.

Half-value layer or thickness: The thickness of an absorbing material required to reduce the intensity of a beam of incident radiation to one-half of its original intensity.

Image: Visual representation of a test object or scene.

Image enhancement: Any of a variety of image processing steps, used singly or in combination to improve the detectability of objects in an image.

Image processing: Actions applied singly or in combination to an image, in particular the measurement and alteration of image features by computer. Also called picture processing.

Image quality indicator: Strip of material the same composition as that of the material being tested, representing a percentage of object thickness and provided with a combination of steps, holes or slots or alternatively made as a series of wires. When placed in the path of the radiation, its image provides a check on the radiographic technique used.

In-motion radiography: Technique in which either the object being radiographed or the source of radiation is in motion during the exposure.

Indication: Nondestructive testing response that requires interpretation to determine its relevance.

Indication, discontinuity: Visible evidence of a material discontinuity. Subsequent interpretation is required to determine the significance of an indication.

Indication, false: (1) Indication produced by something other than a discontinuity or test-object configuration. (2) Indication caused by misapplied or improper technique.

Indication, nonrelevant: Indication caused by a condition that does not affect the usability of the object (a change of section, for instance).

Indication, relevant: Indication from a discontinuity (as opposed to a nonrelevant indication) requiring evaluation by a qualified technician, typically with reference to an acceptance standard, by virtue of the discontinuity's size or location.

Inherent discontinuities: Discontinuities that are produced in the material at the time it is formed (for example, during solidification from the molten state).

Interpretation: Determination of the significance of nondestructive testing indications from the standpoint of their relevance or nonrelevance.

Inverse square law: From a point source of radiation, the intensity of energy decreases as the inverse square of distance from the source increases and vice versa.

Ionizing radiation: Form of radiation that can displace orbital electrons from atoms. Types include X-rays, gamma rays and particles such as neutrons, electrons and alpha particles.

IQI: See **Image quality indicator**.

Iridium-192 (Ir-192): Radioactive isotope of the element iridium, having a half-life of 73 to 75 days and primary photon energies of 0.31 MeV, 0.47 MeV and 0.66 MeV.

Latent image: A condition produced and persisting in the image receptor by exposure to radiation and able to be converted into a visible image by processing.

Level, acceptance: In contrast to rejection level, test level above or below which, depending on the test parameter, test objects are acceptable.

Level, rejection: Value established for indication or test signal above or below which, depending on the test parameter, test objects are rejectable or otherwise distinguished from the remaining objects.

Linear accelerator: High-frequency electron generator.

Material noise: Random signals caused by the material structure of the test object. A component of background noise.

Mechanical properties: Properties of a material that reveal its elastic and inelastic behavior where force is applied, thereby indicating its suitability for mechanical applications (for example, modulus of elasticity, tensile strength, elongation, hardness and fatigue limit).

Milliroentgen: A radiation dose measurement replaced by sievert. 100 000 mR = 1 Sv.

Neutron: Uncharged elementary particle with mass nearly equal to that of the proton.

Neutron radiography: Radiographic testing using a neutron beam.

Neutron radioscopy: Radioscopy using a neutron beam.

Noise: Any undesired signals that tend to interfere with normal detection or processing of a desired signal.

Nondestructive testing (NDT): Determination of the physical condition of an object without affecting that object's ability to fulfill its intended function. Nondestructive testing techniques typically use a probing energy to determine material properties or to indicate the presence of material discontinuities (surface, internal or concealed).

Nonrelevant indication: See **Indication, nonrelevant.**

One hundred percent testing: Testing of all parts of an entire production lot in a prescribed manner. Compare **Sampling, partial.**

Orientation: Angular relationship of a surface, plane, discontinuity or axis to a reference plane or surface.

Pair production: The process whereby a gamma photon with energy greater than 1 MeV is converted directly into matter in the form of an electron-positron pair. Subsequent annihilation of the positron results in the production of two 0.5 MeV gamma photons.

Peripheral vision: Seeing of objects displaced from the primary line of sight and outside the central visual field.

Photoelectric effect: Emission of free electrons from a surface bombarded by sufficiently energetic photons. Such emissions may be used in an illuminance meter and may be calibrated in lux.

Photon: Quantum of electromagnetic radiation.

Photoreceptor: Photon sensor. Examples include film and electronic detector elements.

Physical properties: Nonmechanical properties such as density, electrical conductivity, heat conductivity and thermal expansion.

Pixel: One element of a digital image. Each pixel represents a finite area in the scene being imaged.

Primary radiation: Radiation emitting directly from the target of an X-ray tube or from a radioactive source.

Process: Repeatable sequence of actions to bring about a desired result.

Process control: Application of quality control principles to the management of a repeated process.

Process testing: Initial product testing to establish correct manufacturing procedures and then by periodic tests to ensure that the process continues to operate correctly.

Qualification: Process of demonstrating that an individual has the required amount and the required type of training, experience, knowledge and abilities. May also apply to the qualification of a test technique, process or instrument. See also **Qualified.**

Quality: Ability of a process or product to meet specifications or expectations of its users in terms of efficiency, appearance, longevity and ergonomics.

Quality assurance: Administrative actions that specify, enforce and verify a quality control program.

Quality control: Physical and administrative actions required to ensure compliance with the quality assurance program. May include nondestructive testing in the manufacturing cycle.

Rad: Radiation absorbed dose. Unit of absorbed dose of ionizing radiation. One rad is equal to the absorption of 100 erg (10^{-5} J) of radiation energy per gram of matter associated with human tissue or a biological system. Replaced by the gray (Gy).

Radiation safety officer: Individual supervising a program to provide radiation protection. The representative appointed by the licensee for liaison with the applicable regulatory agency.

Radiographer: Person who performs, supervises and is responsible for industrial radiographic testing operations.

Radiographic equivalence factor: That factor by which the thickness of a material must be multiplied in order to determine what thickness of a standard material (often steel) will have the same absorption.

Radiographic interpretation: Determination of the cause and significance of indications on a radiograph.

Radiographic screens: Fluorescent sheets or lead used to intensify the effect of radiation on films. The screens can be made of a fluorescent metal. Metallic screens help absorb secondary and scattered radiation, which helps to improve image quality.

Radiologic testing (RT): Penetrating radiant energy in the form of X-rays, gamma rays or neutrons for nondestructive testing of objects to provide images of the objects' interiors. Also called radiography. In *SNT-TC-1A* (2001), radiographic testing is considered a technique of the radiologic testing method.

Radiography: Radiologic testing.

Radiology: Science of electromagnetic radiation, particularly ionizing radiation.

Radioscopy: Radiographic testing technique in which gamma rays, X-rays or neutrons are used to produce an image on a video or screen display as opposed to a latent image on a film. The test object or interrogating optics may move in real time to present a moving radiographic image.

Recommended practice: Set of guidelines or recommendations.

Recommended Practice No. SNT-TC-1A: Set of guidelines for employers to establish and conduct a nondestructive testing personnel qualification and certification program. *SNT-TC-1A* was first issued in 1968 by the Society for Nondestructive Testing (SNT, now ASNT) and has been revised every few years since.

Rejection level: See **Level, rejection**.

Relevant indication: See **Indication, relevant**.

Rem: Roentgen equivalent mammal (formerly, man). Unit of absorbed radiation dose in biological matter. It is equal to the absorbed dose in rad multiplied by the quality factor of the radiation.

Repeatability: Ability to reproduce a detectable indication in separate processings and tests from a constant source.

Resolution: Aspect of image quality pertaining to a system's ability to reproduce objects, often measured by resolving a pair of adjacent objects or parallel lines.

Resolution, discontinuity: Property of a test system that enables the separation of indications caused by discontinuities located in close proximity to each other in a test object.

Resolution test: Procedure wherein a line or a series of lines or line pairs are detected to verify or evaluate a system's sensitivity.

Resolution threshold: Minimum distance between a pair of points or parallel lines when they can be distinguished as two, not one, expressed in minutes of arc. Vision acuity in such a case is the reciprocal of one-half of the period expressed in minutes.

Resolving power: Ability of detection systems to separate two points in time or distance. Resolving power depends on the angle of vision and the distance of the sensor from the test surface. Resolving power in vision systems is often measured using parallel lines. Compare **Resolution**.

Roentgen (R): Unit for measurement of radiation intensity; amount of radiation that will generate one electrostatic unit in 1 cm^3 of air at standard atmospheric conditions. The roentgen (R) has been replaced by an SI compound unit, coulomb per kilogram (C·kg^{-1}).

Sampling, partial: Testing of less than 100% of a production lot. See also **One hundred percent testing**.

Sampling, random partial: Partial sampling that is fully random.

Sampling, specified partial: Partial sampling in which a particular frequency or sequence of sample selection is prescribed. An example of specified partial sampling is the testing of every fifth unit.

Scattering: Random reflection and refraction of radiation caused by interaction with material it strikes or penetrates.

Sensitivity: Measure of a sensor's ability to detect small signals. Limited by the signal-to-noise ratio.

Sensor, X-ray: In radiographic testing, device or material that changes with and provides evidence of contact with ionizing radiation. Examples include X-ray film, X-ray sensitive phosphors and electronic devices such as linear detector arrays.

Shielding: Material or object used to reduce intensity of or exposure to penetrating radiation.

SI: International system of measurement based on seven units: meter (m), kilogram (kg), second (s), kelvin (K), ampere (A), candela (cd) and mole (mol).

Sievert (Sv): SI unit for measurement of exposure to ionizing radiation, replacing rem. 1 Sv = 1 J·kg^{-1} = 100 rem.

Signal: Response containing relevant information.

Signal processing: Acquisition, storage, analysis, alteration and output of digital data through a computer.

Signal-to-noise ratio: Ratio of signal values (responses that contain relevant information) to baseline noise values (responses that contain nonrelevant information). See **Noise**.

Source: Machine or material from which ionizing radiation emanates.

Specification: Set of instructions or standards to govern the results or performance of a specific set of tasks or products.

Spectrum: (1) Amplitude distribution of frequencies in a signal. (2) Representation of radiant energy in adjacent bands of hues in sequence according to the energy's wavelengths or frequencies. A rainbow is a well-known example of the visible light spectrum.

Spot check tests: Testing a number of objects from a lot to determine the lot's quality, the sample size being chosen arbitrarily, such as 5% or 10%. This does not provide accurate assurance of the lot's quality.

Spot examination: Local examination of welds or castings.

Standard: (1) Physical object with known material characteristics used as a basis for comparison, specification or calibration. (2) Concept established by authority, custom or agreement to serve as a model or rule in the measurement of quantity or the establishment of a practice or procedure. (3) Document to control and govern practices in an industry or application, applied on a national or international basis and usually produced by consensus. See also **Acceptance standard**.

Stepped wedge: Reference object, with steps of various thicknesses in the range of the test objects' thicknesses, for the radiographic testing of objects having thickness variations or complex geometries. The stepped wedge must be made of material radiographically similar to that of the radiographic test object and may include image quality indicator features (such as calibrated holes) in any or all steps.

Stereo imaging: Imaging technique involving the capture and display of two images of the same object from different angles. Binocular viewing simultaneously of the two images simulates 3D viewing.

Stereoradiography: Radiographic testing using stereo imaging.

Subject contrast: The ratio (or the logarithm of the ratio) of the radiation intensities transmitted by selected portions of the test object.

Survey meter: Portable instrument that measures rate of exposure dose or ionizing radiation intensity.

Target: That part of the anode of an X-ray emitting tube that is hit by the electron beam.

Tenth-value layer or thickness: The thickness of the layer of a specified substance that, when introduced into the path of a given narrow beam of radiation, reduces the intensity of this radiation by a factor of ten.

Threshold level: Setting of an instrument that causes it to register only those changes in response greater or less than a specified magnitude.

Tolerance: Permissible deviation or variation from exact dimensions or standards.

Tube current: The transfer of electricity, created by the flow of electrons, from the filament to the anode target in an X-ray tube; usually expressed in milliamperes.

Unsharpness, geometric: Fuzziness or lack of definition in a radiographic image resulting from the source size, object-to-film distance and the source-to-object distance.

Video presentation: Electronic screen presentation in which radiofrequency signals have been rectified and usually filtered.

X-ray: Penetrating electromagnetic radiation emitted when the inner orbital electrons of an atom are excited and release energy. Radiation is nonisotopic in origin and is generated by bombarding a metallic target with high-speed charged particles, usually electrons.

X-ray diffraction: Radiographic testing technique used for material characterization, based on change in scattering of X-radiation as a result of interaction with test material. See also **Diffraction**.

X-ray fluorescence: Radiographic testing technique used for material characterization, based on wavelengths of fluorescence from material irradiated by X-rays.